JOINT INFORMATION SERVICE PUBLICATIONS

Rehabilitating the Mentally Ill in the Community: A Study of Psychosocial Rehabilitation Centers, by Raymond M. Glasscote, M.A., Elaine Cumming, Ph.D., Irvin D. Rutman, Ph.D., James N. Sussex, M.D., and Sidney M. Glassman, Ph.D. 1971.

Salary Ranges of Personnel Employed in State Mental Hospitals and Community Mental Health Centers—1970, prepared by Charles K. Kanno and Patricia L. Scheidemandel. 1970.

The Staff of the Mental Health Center: A Field Study, by Raymond M. Glasscote, M.A., and Jon E. Gudeman, M.D. 1969.

The Community Mental Health Center: An Interim Appraisal, by Raymond M. Glasscote, M.A., James N. Sussex, M.D., Elaine Cumming, Ph.D., and Lauren H. Smith, M.D. 1969.

Partial Hospitalization for the Mentally Ill: A Study of Programs and Problems, by Raymond M. Glasscote, M.A., Alan M. Kraft, M.D., Sidney M. Glassman, Ph.D., and William W. Jepson, M.D. 1969.

The Mentally Ill Offender: A Survey of Treatment Programs, by Patricia L. Scheidemandel and Charles K. Kanno. 1969.

Legal Services and Community Mental Health Centers, by Henry Weihofen, J.S.D. 1969.

Health Insurance for Mental Illness, by Patricia L. Scheidemandel, Charles K. Kanno, and Raymond M. Glasscote. 1968.

The Treatment of Alcoholism: A Study of Programs and Problems, by Raymond M. Glasscote, M.A., Thomas F. A. Plaut, Ph.D., Donald W. Hammersley, M.D., Francis J. O'Neill, M.D., Morris E. Chafetz, M.D., and Elaine Cumming, Ph.D. 1967.

Approaches to the Care of Long-Term Mental Patients, by Helen Padula, M.S.W., Raymond M. Glasscote, M.A., and Elaine Cumming, Ph.D. 1968.

The Psychiatric Emergency: A Study of Patterns of Service, by Raymond M. Glasscote, M.A., Elaine Cumming, Ph.D., Donald W. Hammersley, M.D., Lucy D. Ozarin, M.D., and Lauren H. Smith, M.D. 1966.

General Hospital Psychiatric Units: A National Survey, by Raymond M. Glasscote and Charles K. Kanno. 1965.

Private Psychiatric Hospitals: A National Survey, by Charles K. Kanno and Raymond M. Glasscote. 1966.

The Community Mental Health Center: An Analysis of Existing Models, by Raymond M. Glasscote, M.A., David Sanders, M.D., M.P.H., H. M. Forstenzer, M.S., and A. R. Foley, M.D. 1964.

ii

HALFWAY HOUSES FOR THE MENTALLY ILL

A Study of Programs and Problems

HALFWAY HOUSES FOR THE MENTALLY ILL
A Study of Programs and Problems

RAYMOND M. GLASSCOTE, M.A.
Chief, Joint Information Service

JON E. GUDEMAN, M.D.
Associate Director, Southard Clinic,
Massachusetts Mental Health Center
Assistant Professor of Psychiatry,
Harvard Medical School

J. RICHARD ELPERS, M.D.
Deputy Director,
Consultation and Education,
Orange County (California)
Community Mental Health Services
Assistant Clinical Professor,
Department of Psychiatry and
Human Behavior,
University of California, Irvine

in collaboration
with

DONALD MILES, Ed.D.
Chief Program Analyst,
New York State Department
of Mental Hygiene

IRVIN D. RUTMAN, Ph.D.
Executive Director,
Horizon House, Philadelphia

MABEL PALMER, M.S.W.
Executive Director, Louisiana
Association for Mental Health

KENT S. MILLER, Ph.D.
Professor of Psychology and
Sociology and Director
of the Community Mental
Health Research Center,
Florida State University

Foreword by
BERTRAM S. BROWN, M.D.
Director, National Institute of Mental Health

A publication of
THE JOINT INFORMATION SERVICE
of the
AMERICAN PSYCHIATRIC ASSOCIATION
and the
NATIONAL ASSOCIATION FOR MENTAL HEALTH
WASHINGTON, D.C., 1971

THE JOINT INFORMATION SERVICE
of the AMERICAN PSYCHIATRIC ASSOCIATION
and the NATIONAL ASSOCIATION FOR MENTAL HEALTH

EXECUTIVE COMMITTEE

For the
National Association for
Mental Health

HON. LUTHER A. ALVERSON,
  Chairman 1970-71
CHARLES FRAZIER
MRS. WINTHROP ROCKEFELLER
HENRY WEIHOFEN, J.S.D.
BRIAN O'CONNELL, *Ex-officio*
  (Executive Director, NAMH)

For the
American Psychiatric Association

ALAN I. LEVENSON, M.D.
PAUL HUSTON, M.D.
JACK R. EWALT, M.D.
LAWRENCE C. KOLB, M.D.
WALTER E. BARTON, M.D.
  Ex-officio
  (Medical Director, APA)

STAFF

RAYMOND M. GLASSCOTE
  Chief
CHARLES K. KANNO
  Research Associate

PATRICIA L. SCHEIDEMANDEL
  Research Associate
LINDA B. PARKER
  Research Assistant

MARJORIE HOLTZCLAW
Information Assistant

Donald W. Hammersley, M.D., serves as permanent professional consultant to the Joint Information Service.

The Joint Information Service is administratively attached to the APA Division of Public Affairs, which is headed by Robert L. Robinson.

Additional copies of this publication are available from THE JOINT INFORMATION SERVICE, 1700 18th Street, N.W., Washington, D.C. 20009, at $6.00, with discount for quantity purchases.

The study reported herein was carried out under a cost-sharing contract between the National Institute of Mental Health and the Joint Information Service. Approximately three quarters of the funds for the project were furnished under Public Health Service Contract No. PH-43-67-1322.

FOREWORD

BERTRAM S. BROWN, M.D., DIRECTOR
NATIONAL INSTITUTE OF MENTAL HEALTH

IN THE MID-1960's, I collaborated in a sociocultural and clinical study of a transitional aftercare residence for psychiatric patients. Published under the title *Halfway House*, this was one of the first attempts on the part of research investigators in the United States to analyze the effects of a protected living environment on mental patients who had been hospitalized and who were attempting to use the halfway house as a steppingstone to personal and social restoration.

There were few such living facilities in existence in 1965 when the study of Rutland Corner House residents was published. Since that time the number has increased, but within the professional mental health community interest in long-term rehabilitation of the mentally ill has lagged behind interest in short-term, crisis-oriented therapy. For anyone concerned with social psychiatry, therefore, this volume will be surprising and exciting. It is my considered guess that it will stimulate further development of halfway houses among a growing number of advocates of the mentally ill who believe that mental patients have not only a right to treatment, but also a right to live in a community.

In this new study, sponsored by the Joint Information Service, the authors illustrate quite definitely that the concept of the halfway house has been significantly developed into operational living situations offering "a humane, compassionate, empathic environment badly needed by a sizable number of people who leave state hospitals."

This development stems from efforts and concern on the part of a comparatively small number of individuals to find less traumatizing, alienating, and costly forms of service than traditional hospitalization. In their considered judgment, the authors of this study have come to the conclusion that the state hospital patient population can be *substantially further reduced* by the expansion of the halfway house experience. The data on which the authors based this conclusion make up the content of this book. As a narrative, it is evocative and provocative. It is not my purpose here to present a critical review; however, on the basis of my long and continuing interest in social and community psychiatry, I cannot resist some brief comments on the meaning of this study—in terms of future developments for communities, for mental health facilities, for mental health training of manpower, for funding of services, and for the patients themselves. Simultaneously, I hesitate to do this, because, as the authors comment, perhaps the advance of the halfway house in the past five or six years has been achieved *because* of a lack of official guidelines and because of the fact that there is no official definition of a halfway house which states what such a facility must or must not provide.

Anyone who reads this volume will be impressed by the humanism on which the operation of these facilities is based, under—in many instances—informal and catch-as-catch-can conditions of supervision, funding, and material resources. One must wonder to what extent such a humanism can flourish under official limitations that might hamper imaginative explorations. At the same time, however, if data on staffing, on costs, and on progress of patients reported here can be adapted to more communities, the experiment must be broadened to provide services to more people.

The halfway houses discussed are of two kinds: *a*) those providing a transitional residence for patients, following hospitalization, who, after an average stay of four to six months, can leave the halfway house for autonomous living within the community and who can be trained through what the authors aptly term "survival skills" to maintain themselves productively in a community. This "survival" training can and does range from such things as how to ride a bus or how to shop for food to job training; and *b*) long-term sheltered living arrangements which may indeed be permanent substitutes for hospitalization for individuals who can be maintained in the community with continuing supportive help. These investigators conclude that both types are necessary and can be appropriately developed to serve more people.

In this context, the authors list as appropriate services the provision of a smooth transition from hospital to community; permanent placement; a means for initiating release from hospitals; an alternative to hospitalization; a means to shorten the length of inpatient treatment.

Most of the individuals who have been helped through the halfway house experience are victims of some form of schizophrenia "who seem to need the experience of living in a specialized transitional setting." However, staffs of halfway houses informed the investigators that in selecting residents, they considered behavior more important than diagnosis, and commented further that the length of hospitalization does not seem to be a factor in the outcome of successful rehabilitation. This finding is apparently based in large part on continuation of psychoactive medication, since, as one three-year study showed, in every instance in which a patient returned to the hospital, it was because of failure to follow a prescribed drug regimen.

Of great interest to mental health professionals involved in the training of mental health manpower is evidence in these studies that staffing of halfway houses illustrates "the practice of engaging employees who appear to have the personal characteristics and assets helpful in dealing with people who have a history of mental illness, but who are trained at the lowest level consistent with the kinds of responsibilities and duties they must carry."

The authors attribute this attitude in part to "an antiprofessional sentiment that is pronounced in many of the mental health facilities we have visited in the past several years."

This phenomenon is complex and goes beyond the scope of this study, but the authors suggest some of the contributing factors, which are relevant to the training of manpower in the 1970's. Among them "appear to be: a dissatisfaction with the outcome of historic professional interventions with the mentally ill; a concern that prolonged training inculcates an emphasis on pathology which limits the professional's capacity to recognize and work with the healthy aspects of the patient; a questioning of the whole idea of formal training that abounds in colleges all over the country; and an almost defiant assertion that 'good' and 'positive' personal characteristics are more important than professional training."

As the authors point out, the person who has earned a master's or even a bachelor's degree in a behavioral or social science is not, after all, so "minimally trained." However, the point I wish to make here is that, if indeed, these less-than-doctoral-level staff can function well, the cost of staffing a larger number of halfway houses would be significantly lowered. Experience with "indigenous personnel" in community mental health centers and neighborhood health centers has also demonstrated the validity of such staffing practices, and further manpower studies should be initiated to test this experience.

One of the major services the authors of this study have achieved is to present some comparative cost data. Costs and funding patterns for each of the houses described are presented in this volume. The general conclusions indicate that a day in a halfway house costs approximately one half as much as a day in a state hospital; one fourth or less of the cost in a psychiatric unit of a general hospital; and in most cases less than the cost in a day hospital.

Funding patterns range from plans by which state divisions of vocational rehabilitation are reimbursed by as much as eighty percent by the federal government, to community participation achieved on a continuing basis by one knowledgeable and dedicated woman. The lessons to be learned and the information available for widespread utilization are here for the taking.

At a time when the cost of health care is skyrocketing and the quality of health care is too often impersonal, to read this book is to realize that some of the traditional, neighborly helping techniques work just as well as they ever did—technology or no technology.

Washington, D.C.
January 1971

CONTENTS

I. Introduction

BY 1970, IN AT LEAST 90 CITIES AND TOWNS in the United States, there were 128 or more "halfway houses" providing specialized places to live for people who are or have been mentally ill. While the combined capacity of halfway houses is a tiny fraction of the inpatient census of mental hospitals, the increased rate at which they are being established suggests that this new locus for serving the mentally ill, considered little more than a curiosity a decade ago, carries the promise of becoming a major consideration in the continued redirection of mental illness services during the years immediately ahead.

HALFWAY HOUSES FOR THE MENTALLY ILL are new in the United States. The British began their efforts with "hostels" in the nineteenth century, but in this country, there were by 1950 only two "halfway houses," neither operating in the "contemporary" sense.[1] The first in the current concept seems to have been Rutland Corner House in Boston. This facility since the 1870's had provided shelter to distressed women. In the 1950's a reassessment was made of its purposes and goals, and among the various suggestions for redirecting its program was one from Dr. Harry Solomon, then superintendent of Massachusetts Mental Health Center, that it be used for selected patients leaving that hospital. Thus in 1954 it began to cater specifically to women with a history of mental illness.

There seem to have been no more than ten halfway houses by 1960. When Raush and Raush[2] did their 1963 survey, they were able to locate 40. And more than half of 128 that participated in our own survey in 1969 had been established in the three and a half years prior to the survey (Figure 1).

---

[1] Gould Farm, established in Great Barrington, Massachusetts, in 1913, and Spring Lake Ranch, established in Cuttingsville, Vermont, in 1932, are both designed as "self-sufficient" communities, in rural settings, providing an atmosphere strongly reminiscent of the Moral Treatment movement of the nineteenth century.

[2] H. L. Raush and C. L. Raush: *The Halfway House Movement: A Search for Sanity*. Appleton-Century-Crofts, New York, 1968.

1

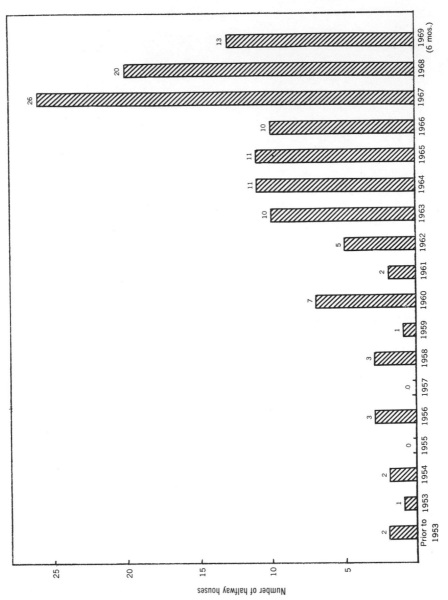

Fig. 1. Year began operation, 127 halfway houses.

Wᴇ ᴀɢʀᴇᴇ ᴡɪᴛʜ Rᴀᴜsʜ ᴀɴᴅ Rᴀᴜsʜ that halfway houses for the mentally ill have become a "movement." But it seems to be a loose, highly individual, largely undirected movement. There have been various forms of support to halfway houses from various levels of government, but by and large there have not been official definitions of what comprises a halfway house, nor of what it must or may not provide. There is no national association of halfway houses,[3] and the only state association that we know of is the one in California. There is no accrediting body. In the occupancy and residency codes of most municipalities, halfway houses do not even exist (so that they become licensed as boardinghouses, apartment houses, and even taverns).

Some of the mental health professionals who became involved with halfway houses in the pioneering days of the 1950's expressed convictions about boundaries they thought should be set; for example, it was maintained that a facility located on the grounds of a hospital ought not to be considered a halfway house, or that in order to be considered a halfway house a program should be required to have salaried, live-in staff. As additional sponsors planned additional halfway houses, some, both through personal visits and from descriptions in the literature, deliberately drew on the experience of such important pioneer facilities as Woodley House in Washington, D.C., Rutland Corner House in Boston, Wellmet in Cambridge, the rehabilitation houses associated with Vermont State Hospital, Conard House in San Francisco, and The Quarters in Santa Clara (see Bibliography). Others seem to have been developed almost entirely according to specific local needs, resources, and purposes. In any case, halfway houses are characterized by a great deal of individuality, and even among the few that we visited during this survey we found many interesting variations and imaginative explorations that might have been hampered if official limitations had been imposed. Indeed, one might conclude that the greatest advantage that the halfway house movement has enjoyed during its forward surge of the 1960's has been precisely the lack of official guidelines.

While we necessarily formulated our own working definitions for the purposes of this study, we believe it would be disadvantageous at this early time to impose definitions and limits, since a great deal of exploration in staffing patterns, selection criteria, and therapeutic capability still needs to be made.

------

[3] There is, however, an international association of halfway houses headquartered in Canada, whose membership consists largely of halfway houses for offenders.

II. Why and How This Study Was Done

SINCE 1963, THE JOINT INFORMATION SERVICE has been conducting a series of studies of aspects of community-based mental health services, with particular reference to facilities funded under the federal program of support to *community mental health centers.* These studies have led to several publications, which are listed on p. ii.

Throughout these investigations we have been impressed with the accumulating evidence of the success with which the mental health field is redirecting service to people with serious mental illness, from the long-term hospitalization in state facilities which was characteristic of a generation ago to the now widespread practice of providing immediate, locally based treatment that frequently avoids hospitalization altogether.

We will not recapitulate here the various advances of the state-of-the-art or the emergence of new attitudes toward the mentally ill which were involved in this redirection. This has been done in a number of places. The reader unfamiliar with such developments as the growth of general hospital psychiatry, the lessons learned from military psychiatry during World War II, the introduction of new categories of "psychoactive" medications in the 1950's, the work of the Joint Commission on Mental Illness and Health, the passage of the Community Mental Health Centers Act in 1963, and so on, will find a brief account of how things were by the mid-1960's in our own publication, *The Community Mental Health Center: An Analysis of Existing Models.*[1] The ensuing years have been marked by continued progress, particularly in terms of implementing the program of federal support for local services and the growth in the number of voluntary health insurance policies providing benefits for private treatment of mental illness.

What is mainly involved in this redirection of mental illness services, it seems to us, is a basic change of attitude about the rights of the mentally ill. A generation ago, mental illness was widely viewed as not amenable to treatment, as characteristically long-term if not lifelong;

---

[1] R. M. Glasscote, D. Sanders, H. M. Forstenzer, and A. R. Foley: *The Community Mental Health Center: An Analysis of Existing Models.* Joint Information Service, Washington, D.C., 1964.

for those who could not afford a private mental hospital, the state hospital was seen as the locus of choice. Today a great percentage of mental health professionals and many political leaders and influential laymen are committed to the idea that the mentally ill not only should be treated in the local community, but that they have a *right* to be there unless they are demonstrably dangerous (as few are), and that they are *entitled* to the various kinds of supports that they need in order to remain there and to derive some meaning and satisfaction from life.

More and more this persuasion is being translated into a reality. Over the past fourteen years the number of patients in state mental hospitals has declined by 34 percent, from a high of 559,000 to a figure in 1969 of 367,000, while during the same period the population of the country has increased by 23 percent. This does not mean that the incidence or the prevalence of mental illness has decreased; it means that mentally ill people are increasingly being treated in community facilities. (It also means, as Donald Miles points out, that many state hospitals have themselves developed a "community orientation." The increase in the number of community treatment agencies has been accompanied by the development within a number of state hospitals of geographic unitization of service and outpatient programs of considerable size.)

A S WE VISITED SCORES OF PROGRAMS in the course of our field studies, we became increasingly aware that as yet most of the emphasis in redirecting treatment to the community has been focused on the acute phase of illness. There has been great progress in many places in making treatment immediately available to the disturbed and agitated patient, to helping him reconstitute, often in only a few days, through an intensive treatment program in a general hospital or a community mental health center. But we were concerned that the development of and enthusiasm for longer-term supporting resources seemed to be lagging considerably behind that of short-term, crisis-oriented, acute treatment services. We are saying here that we believe there is substantial evidence that many of the people who have a history of major mental illness, if they are to survive in the community, require some special services that by and large are unneeded by the general population. Particularly persons with schizophrenia are apt to have marked difficulties in establishing and maintaining successful interdependencies; many of them have no marketable job skills, and their employment records are so poor that they have little prospect of finding jobs; and many do not have access to a suitable living arrangement.

Thus, the very progress that has enabled community-based treating facilities to retain mentally ill people locally and has also enabled state hospitals to treat people briefly and release them to their own communities has at the same time resulted in a build-up of tens of thousands of people who are living marginal lives in the community, frequently relapsing with resultant rehospitalization. This is evidenced by the fact that readmissions as a proportion of all admissions to state hospitals have been steadily rising over the years. Such readmissions now comprise about a third of all the people going into state hospitals. They respond favorably to treatment and are returned to the community, where oftentimes they relapse. The relapse may often be related to the illness and not to the quality of their lives, but there is much evidence that many people relapse because they are not capable, without special support, of working out a satisfactory arrangement for living and working.

W E THUS BECAME CONCERNED with the need to promote interest in these supporting aspects of mental illness services, and the National Institute of Mental Health was immediately responsive to our proposal that, as part of the continuing cost-sharing contract under which our studies have been carried out, we spend a year studying certain kinds of supporting programs.

We decided to investigate two types of support facilities. One was a group of programs that call themselves psychosocial rehabilitation centers, our interest in which arose from our knowledge of the two largest, Fountain House in New York and Horizon House in Philadelphia. These are the subject of a separate report.[2] The other was the halfway house.

T HERE WAS NO CURRENT DIRECTORY of halfway houses. The most recent was that appended to Raush and Raush, based on a 1963 survey, and we felt certain that a large number of additional houses had been established since then. Consequently, in mid-1969, prior to the start of the field study, the Joint Information Service wrote to the directors of each state mental health department and to the executive directors of each of the state mental health associations, requesting that they forward lists of all the facilities in their states believed by them to be half-

---

[2] R. M. Glasscote, E. Cumming, I. D. Rutman, J. N. Sussex, and S. M. Glassman: *Rehabilitating the Mentally Ill in the Community: A Study of Psychosocial Rehabilitation Centers.* Joint Information Service, Washington, D.C., 1971.

way houses accepting people who have a history of mental illness.

Eighty-seven percent responded, providing altogether 209 evidently unduplicated names of facilities. A letter and a brief questionnaire (Appendix I) were sent to each late in 1969; a single follow-up was sent to nonrespondents one month later. Of the 182 respondents:

15 answered "No" to the question, "Do you accept persons who are or have been mentally ill as residents in your halfway house?"

16 answered "Yes" to this question but were eliminated because they added information indicating that they do not accept the general run of mentally ill people but rather specialize in a particular symptom-specific category, notably alcoholics.

13 indicated that they are not halfway houses.

 4 were not yet open.

 4 were alternative names and therefore duplicates.

 2 were no longer in operation.

Some of the respondents were operating more than one halfway house; altogether there were 117 "in scope" responses, representing 128 houses.

The process of selecting those to visit was a relatively simple one. All of the responses were sorted, primarily according to *a*) auspice (state government, local government, private nonprofit, private for profit), *b*) capacity, *c*) whether service was exclusively to the mentally ill or to additional disability groups as well, *d*) whether only one or both sexes were admitted, and *e*) demographic and geographic characteristics of the locale. This categorization led in itself to some almost automatic choices for the field study; for example, there were few proprietary facilities to choose from, and few of large size. A number of the respondents had included copies of annual reports, brochures, reprints of newspaper articles, and other such materials that helped to give an idea whether the program was an active one, well thought of locally, and in any way unusual. In certain categories where there were several candidates and no indication for selecting a particular one to visit, we telephoned mental health professionals in the area whom we knew personally to ask for further information. We were not seeking, and perhaps could not have obtained, a "representative" group of halfway houses; instead we were seeking as much diversity as possible within the stricture that we wanted each program to be of "good" quality, in such respects as appropriate criteria for admission, staffing, financing, and so on.

Each facility selected was then asked if it would be willing to complete for us a more extensive questionnaire (Appendix II) intended to provide background material, and then to receive the authors and consultants for a visit during which we would interview each member of the staff, some of the residents, and some representatives of outside agencies that refer residents or from whom services are obtained for the residents. Each one agreed to participate. The visits were made in February, March, and April of 1970. The authors visited all of the facilities, the consultants the following:

	Miles	Rutman	Palmer	Miller
Gateways, Indianapolis		X		
Roscoe House, Chicago		X		
Cobble Hill Center, New York	X			
Gutman House, Portland, Oregon		X	X	
The Lodge, Denver		X	X	
Magnificat Houses, Houston				X
McKinney House, New Orleans				X
Mental Health Recovery, Belmont, California	X			
Rehabilitation Mental Health Services, Santa Clara, California	X			
Gilead House, Middletown, Connecticut			X	X
Transitional Services, Pittsburgh			X	X

The interviews were recorded on tape and the tapes were transcribed. The authors and consultants also prepared trip reports. The descriptions of each program herein are thus based on a) the orientation questionnaire, b) the transcription of the interviews, and c) the trip reports. Each facility was asked to review the description of its program in order to correct any misstatements or to rebut any critical comments, and each did so.

After the visits were concluded, the authors and consultants met in Washington, D.C., in April 1970, with the directors of eight of these eleven programs. (Budget limitations made it impossible for us to include all eleven.) During a two-day meeting, this group considered and reacted to an agenda the authors had prepared, which they felt reflected the issues and the problems involved in organizing and operating a halfway house for the mentally ill. This conference was recorded on tape and transcribed.

Working principally from *Psychological Abstracts, Index Medicus,* and a print-out furnished by the National Clearinghouse for Mental

Health Information, the staff of the Joint Information Service concurrently carried out a search of the literature of halfway houses. The introductory section of this volume and the final two chapters are thus based primarily on *a*) the two-day conference with eight of the directors, *b*) the literature search, and *c*) our own synthesis, and that of the four consultants, of all that we heard and saw during the course of our field visits.

III. What Is a Halfway House?

PLACES OF RETREAT, SECURITY, AND SHELTER for distressed and afflicted people are centuries old. Monasteries, churches, fortresses, embassies, and orphanages have taken in those who needed protection from some threatening force or from the consequences of their own impairment or weakness. Perhaps the most notable example in this country was the creation of a system of state hospitals in the nineteenth century, originally and idealistically intended to provide asylum ("inviolable sanctuary") to people believed, because of mental illness, to be inadequate to the demands of living in the general society.

Mostly within the past generation, what seems to be a truly new aspect of protective residence has emerged. Community-based facilities known as *halfway houses* have been developed with the intention of providing a particular kind of shelter which, rather than sequester the troubled person from the community, *deliberately prepares him to participate in community life.* Specialized halfway houses have been developed to serve the mentally ill, the mentally retarded, paroled offenders, delinquent juveniles, drug addicts, alcoholics, and the physically handicapped. A number of "multicategory" halfway houses have also been established, providing shelter to various kinds of impaired people, thus evidencing the belief of some that *marginality* is a more binding attribute than one particular form of illness or past behavior.

We have no data that define for us why this new approach to impaired people has come about. We suppose it is largely the combined result of an awareness that past practices with marginal people have not succeeded as well as one would like, and an increased concern, related to a general rise in the level of expectation, with the right of every person to participate as fully as possible in the life of the community.

HALFWAY HOUSES MAY HAVE several concurrent goals and purposes, and houses specializing in particular disability groups can be assumed to vary somewhat in their goals and purposes. For example, one goal of the halfway house that accepts alcoholics would be for its resi-

10

dents to remain sober as much of the time as they are able. The halfway house for paroled offenders would attempt to inculcate the belief that they will be better off by not participating in any further criminal behavior. The halfway house for the mentally retarded would want to teach its residents how to behave in ways that will increase self-esteem and self-realization, while avoiding embarrassment in ordinary social interchanges.

In this study, we are concerned primarily with halfway houses that accept those with a history of serious mental illness—for the most part, persons with psychoses, generally schizophrenia, with depressions, and with severe neuroses. We eliminated from the study those respondents indicating that they accepted only alcoholics or drug users; although we realize that these two symptom-specific diagnoses often fall within the purview of mental health programs, we felt nonetheless that they should be excluded for two reasons: *a*) we believe that there are often important distinguishing characteristics in the "tone" of halfway houses for alcoholics and particularly for drug addicts and *b*) we believe that the problems of alcoholism and illegal drug use are sufficiently large in scope as to deserve separate study.

Our criterion for considering a respondent "in scope" was simply whether it indicated that it accepted either the mentally ill only, or the mentally ill plus other categories of residents. We did not have at that point, nor do we have now that the study is completed, any criteria about size, location, staff (or lack of it), time limit, auspice, and so on that would entitle us to say, "This is not a halfway house." As it turned out, about half of our respondents were in fact intermixing the mentally ill with other categories, and about 27 percent of the "in scope" respondents were intermixing alcoholics and the mentally ill.

S EVERAL DEFINITIONS HAVE APPEARED in the literature over the years. However, it does not seem useful to go back and review these early definitions since more than half of the halfway houses we identified in our survey were established from 1966 onward. Instead, we propose one of our own.

> A halfway house for the mentally ill is a nonmedical residential facility specifically intended to enhance the capabilities of people who are mentally ill, or who are impaired by residuals of or deficits from mental illness, to remain in the community, participating to the fullest possible extent in community life.

This definition, although already overlong, needs some explication.

1. *A nonmedical residential facility.* In defining the halfway house

as nonmedical, we are not underestimating the role or importance of medical service, as will become clear later. At the simplest, we mean that a medical residential facility is by definition a nursing home or a hospital. More intricately, we think there are some important indications that medical involvement in the halfway house should be of a consultative and backup nature, as we will discuss in the section on staffing a halfway house.

2. *People who are mentally ill.* From what we learned during this study, we think it a mistake to conceive of halfway houses as being exclusively, or even largely, for people who are "recovered" or "recovering" from mental illness. A large percentage of the people living in halfway houses, if brought to a diagnostician, would undoubtedly be diagnosed as presently mentally ill. The more important consideration which emerged, repeatedly, in this study is the *behavior* of the individual; most halfway houses do not seem to care whether the person could be presently fitted out with any particular label, provided he can meet the demands of living in the house.

3. *Impaired by residuals of or deficits from mental illness.* Even for those whose illness is so completely in remission that they would be diagnosed as "non-mentally ill," there is oftentimes a limited capacity for meeting the demands of day-to-day living. This may sometimes be a deficit from the disease process itself. In other cases it may be the result of the loss of social competence through disuse during a long period of hospitalization. Occasionally it may be because a frightened, long-hospitalized person finds the world so greatly changed that he feels unable to cope with it.

4. *To remain in the community.* This is the respect in which we probably depart most from the "traditional" definitions of the halfway house. The pioneers of the 1950's were largely advocates of a transitional, frequently time-limited residence, whose regularly reiterated goal was to equip the individual to move on from the protective environment of the halfway house, either to return to his family, provided he has one that is willing to take him in and is not too stressful, or to move on to some autonomous living arrangement such as sharing an apartment with friends or taking a rented room, provided he will not be overwhelmingly lonely living alone. This will undoubtedly remain a major purpose of halfway houses. What it conceptualizes is a *course* that the patient is intended to navigate, from a dependent life in the hospital to an autonomous life in the community, with the halfway house falling somewhere around the midpoint.

We propose an additional concept, namely, that some halfway houses may also serve as permanent facilities for people who are able to move part way but not fully into the community. We believe there are many people who remain continuously in mental hospitals, and others who move constantly back and forth between community and hospital, who might live more or less continuously in the community were a specialized living arrangement available to them. But many of these may not be employable, either because they are too old, too disorganized, or have no marketable skills, and they may not be capable of acquiring the skills required to live autonomously. Related to this is a growing tendency among state hospitals to discharge people who seem to have received "maximum benefits of hospitalization," regardless of what their prospects in the community may be. Beyond this, there is a growing tendency for statutes relating to mental illness to prohibit the hospitalization of any person not found to be dangerous. As a result of these things, we suspect that there is a growing number of people "excluded" from state hospitals who are living empty lives in the community and whose circumstances would be improved by the good atmosphere that characterizes most of the halfway houses that we know.

(It may be suitable to consider how the halfway house differs from the nursing home and the foster home, since many state hospital patients have been placed in these kinds of facilities. Nursing homes should be reserved for people too deteriorated physically to take care of their own biological needs. Foster homes may be placements of choice for some mentally ill people who seem to need a setting that simulates a normal family group; their suitability will depend both on the quality of the particular foster home and on whether an individual requires more structured group support than some foster homes may be able to provide.)

5. *Participating to the fullest possible extent in community life.* The kinds of people just now described may not be able to participate in community life beyond taking a walk, sitting in the park, visiting the neighborhood library, or participating in some of the group activities planned by volunteers or staff members. But we think they are entitled to live in the community, doing whatever they can.

Many other people with a history of mental illness, as the experience of halfway houses and other types of rehabilitation facilities show,[1] do have the potential, particularly with suitable support along the way, of becoming employed, if not full time, then part time, if not competitively,

[1] R. M. Glasscote, E. Cumming, I. D. Rutman, J. N. Sussex, and S. M. Glassman: *Rehabilitating the Mentally Ill in the Community: A Study of Psychosocial Rehabilitation Centers.* Joint Information Service, Washington, D.C., 1971.

then in a sheltered setting.[2] Many can gradually assume the responsibilities and acquire the skills needed for running a household and can then move on from the halfway house to a more independent living arrangement. Thus, while we believe that the halfway house role should be broadened to include terminal placement, we also believe that halfway houses ought to enhance and foster opportunities for their residents to develop their potential for becoming productive, self-supporting, self-realized members of the general society.

---

[2] Except that in this country there are scarcely any terminal sheltered workshops for the mentally ill.

IV. The Status of Halfway Houses as of 1969

Number and capacity of halfway houses accepting the mentally ill. Eighty-seven percent of the state mental health commissioners and state mental health association directors responded to our request for lists of halfway houses serving the mentally ill, providing a list of 209 facilities. If we assume that the nonrespondents did not differ in any major characteristic from the respondents, then a one hundred percent response would have yielded a list of 239 facilities.

The "in scope" respondents to our survey represented 62 percent of the total survey list. Applying this figure to the projected list of 239 would yield a total of 148 facilities as of mid-1969. We believe that such a projection is reasonable.

The average capacity of respondents was 22 residents. Projecting once more yields a total capacity of 3256. The respondents indicated that 77 percent of their residents were in the mental illness category, which would suggest a total capacity at one time of 2507 mental illness residents.

The number of in-scope respondents who started halfway houses in the first half of 1969 was 13. Assuming that additional ones were established at the same rate during the rest of the year and continuing into 1970, there would be by mid-1970 probably somewhere between 170 and 180 halfway houses that accept the mentally ill, with a total capacity at one time of about 2950 mental illness clients.

Categories of residents served. Fewer than half of the in-scope respondents—47 percent—limit their services to the mentally ill. The remaining 68 facilities intermix people with mental illness and a number of other disability groups. Twenty-seven percent also accept people with a history of alcoholism, and almost as large a group (25 percent) accept the mentally retarded. Eleven percent each accept drug addicts and former convicts; eight percent accept the physically handicapped; and

15

twelve percent accept a variety of other categories. These figures are not mutually exclusive. The most common patterns are these:

	Number of facilities
Mentally ill only	60
Mentally ill, mentally retarded	16
Mentally ill, alcoholics	9
Mentally ill, alcoholics, drug addicts	4
Mentally ill, alcoholics, ex-convicts	4
Mentally ill, physically handicapped	3
Mentally ill, mentally retarded, physically handicapped	3
Mentally ill, mentally retarded, alcoholics	3
Mentally ill, mentally retarded, alcoholics, drug addicts, others	3

An additional 23 facilities accept residents according to other patterns.

Year of opening. More than half the responding facilities were established during the three and a half years prior to our survey.

Ten facilities (eight percent of respondents) began operating during the 1950's. Forty-six facilities (36 percent) began operating between 1960 and the end of 1965. Sixty-nine facilities (54 percent) were established from 1966 onward.

Sex of residents. Three fifths of the respondents—77 facilities or 62 percent—accept both men and women as residents. Thirty facilities, or 24 percent, accept women only, and 17 facilities, or 14 percent, accept men only.

Capacity of the house. The capacity of the respondents ranged from four to 200, with an average of 22, a median of 17, a mode of 12. A little more than half—53 percent, or 63 facilities—accommodate between 11 and 20 people. Only 14 percent accommodate ten or fewer residents, and only nine percent accommodate more than 40. A more complete breakdown is given in Figure 2.

Age limits. Only about a quarter of the respondents—36 facilities or 28 percent—said that they have no stipulated age limits, and among these, of course, there are some age-related behavioral criteria, such as being ambulatory or employable. There were 91 facilities that reported an age limit. Fifty-seven of these indicated a lower limit only, and 34 set both an upper and a lower limit. None set an upper limit only. Three quarters of those stipulating a lower age limit set it at 16, 17, or 18.

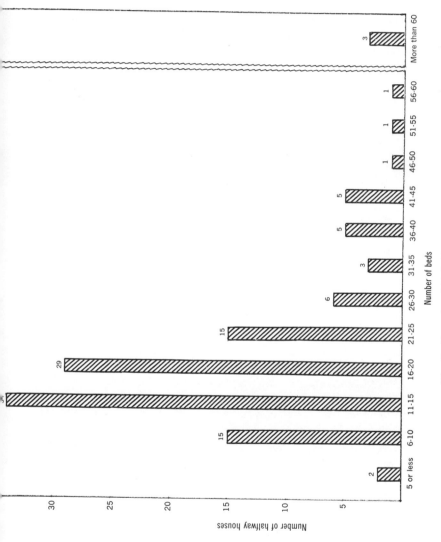

Fig. 2. Capacity, 120 halfway houses.

Eight of the respondents were operating programs specifically for younger clients; four of these, catering to teen-agers, set both lower and upper limits accordingly, and four others, serving young adults, set limits in the range of about 18 to 35. There did not seem to be any respondents specializing in service to the aged; furthermore, 11 respondents said that they do not accept residents over the age of 65, and another 12 set upper limits between 55 and 65.

Exclusions. Just as there are many houses that specifically include certain "special problem" disability groups, so there are some that specifically exclude them. Of the respondents furnishing information about exclusions, almost three fifths (74 facilities or 59 percent) said they did not exclude "any particular categories of persons who are or have been mentally ill." The 51 facilities indicating one or more excluded categories fell into 32 patterns, most of them involving only one or two facilities. We did not furnish a check list, but rather left it to the respondent to name his own categories. The category most commonly excluded was the alcoholic, indicated by 18 percent, followed by the drug addict, at 14 percent. Sex deviates were listed by 11 percent, mental retardates by seven percent, sociopaths by six percent, those who have no potential to work or live independently by six percent, aggressive "acting out" people by five percent, and the physically handicapped, suicidal-homicidal and geriatric by three percent each. Epileptics, arsonists, psychotics, ex-convicts, and "those needing supervision" were mentioned by two percent each.

Twenty-nine respondents (23 percent) listed two or more exclusions.

The three most common—alcoholism, drug addiction, and sex deviation—seem, on the basis of our field visits, to be excluded because their behavior is threatening both to fellow residents and to staff, who are apprehensive that such people will interfere with the orderly and harmonious running of the house. However, from our visits we observed that the exclusion, once a person has been accepted as a resident, is more on the basis of *doing* than of *being;* in other words, a person who, it turned out, had a history of alcoholism or drug use would probably not be expelled, provided he did not use illegal drugs or get drunk while living in the house.

Length of stay. The data regarding length of stay are not usable because of problems about the time span used for answering. However, a good deal of incidental data leads us to believe that the average turnover is from two to three times per year (that is, an average stay of four to six months). On this basis, our earlier projection of a mid-1970 capacity of halfway houses for mental patients of about 2950 would lead us to think that somewhere between 5900 and 8850 mental illness clients per year can be served by presently operating halfway houses.

Auspices. More than three fifths of the respondents (77 facilities or 62 percent) operate under voluntary (private nonprofit) auspices; 34 facilities (27 percent) operate under state government; five are private facilities intended to make a profit; one operates under local government; and eight others under combinations of the above.

Of the 34 facilities operated by state government, most appear to be facilities of the state Divisions of Vocational Rehabilitation, particularly in Colorado and Georgia.

Monthly charges to residents. We asked the halfway houses to indicate the minimum monthly charge to residents. The resulting figures must be viewed as extremely relative, since the houses differ so much from one to another in respect of *a*) having subsidies that permit them to charge less than the actual cost for *all* residents, and to make further allowance for people who have limited funds and cannot arrange any form of third-party payment, and *b*) how much service, if any, the program offers in addition to room and board. In any case, two fifths of 80 facilities indicate their minimum charge is $100 or less, and two thirds that it is $150 or less. Only 14 percent have a minimum charge of more than $200 per month.

Sources of funds. The questionnaire asked, "What are the two or three principal sources of funds?" Replies were furnished by all 128 facilities. No check list was provided, so that the respondents used their own categories. About a quarter (35 facilities, or 27 percent) indicated only a single source, the rest indicated two, three, or occasionally four.

The most important source of financing for halfway houses is the federal/state rehabilitation program, under which the federal government reimburses 80 percent of the cost of the services provided by the state Divisions of Vocational Rehabilitation. The perceptions of where the money comes from appear to vary, with some programs identifying it as state derived, and others, who are aware that the original source is the federal government, as federally derived. In any case, 81 facilities (63 percent) indicated either the Division of Vocational Rehabilitation or the Social and Rehabilitation Service (the name of the federal agency). (Another 20, or 16 percent, stated "the federal government," and a number of these responses probably refer to the federal-state rehabilitation program.)

The next largest source is rent and fees, mentioned by 57 respondents (45 percent). If what we found in our field interviews holds true for the total group, this represents not only funds paid in by residents from their own earnings or savings, but also funds which the residents receive from the welfare department, Social Security disability pensions, Vocational Rehabilitation maintenance stipends, and various other third-party sources.

Fifteen facilities, or twelve percent, indicated that grants are a principal source of funds. Nine (seven percent) named the local government.

(As discussed later, substantially all halfway houses have to rely on outside funds. By and large it does not seem that halfway houses can be supported entirely from payments from residents.)

Program and services. The facilities were asked to indicate any programs or services they provide or sponsor other than sheltered residential placement. No check list was provided. Among the 125 respondents, 24 facilities (19 percent) indicated they do not provide or sponsor anything else. The others are engaged in a variety of additional activities, as follows:

	Number of facilities	Percent
Vocational services	46	37
Counseling/guidance	29	23
Group therapy	19	15
"General program"	17	14
"Follow-up"	13	10
Recreational activities	10	8
Sheltered workshop	9	7
Social club	9	7
Housing and community placement	8	6
Medical services	7	6
Individual therapy	7	6
"Mental health center connection"	6	5
Volunteer program	6	5
Other	7	6

Community mental health center affiliation. The facilities were asked to indicate whether "you are in any way related to or affiliated with a federally assisted community mental health center." All 128 responded; of these, 16 (13 percent) indicated such an affiliation.

Referral sources. The facilities were asked to indicate "the principal sources from which mental illness residents are referred to you." All 128 responded, with 46 (36 percent) listing a single "principal" source, the other 82 (64 percent) listing two or more. The average number indicated per facility was two.

The most common referral source was state hospitals, indicated by 98 respondents (77 percent). Next came psychiatrists in private practice, listed by 42 (33 percent), the Division of Vocational Rehabilitation (25 facilities, 20 percent), community mental health centers (23 facilities, 18 percent), private hospitals (21 facilities, 16 percent), "counselors" (presumably for the most part vocational rehabilitation counselors) (17 facilities, 13 percent). The only other category was self-referrals, mentioned by only four respondents (three percent).

Number of staff. We asked the facilities to list the members of their staff, and 124 did so. Many were part-time employees, and because of the problems of categorization we have not attempted to convert these to full-time equivalencies. The 101 facilities indicating full-time employees reported a total of 503, an average of five each. As indicated, the average capacity of the houses was 22, which would indicate one full-time staff member for every 4.4 residents. For a facility providing only room and board, this ratio would seem high; but many of the houses reported that they provide a variety of other services, and this doubtless accounts for part of the seemingly "rich" staffing. Also, we know from our site visits that in some programs the staff carry long-term follow-up responsibility for former residents.

We did not provide a check list of personnel but rather relied on the facilities to use their own job titles. In the responses there was probably some overlap or duplication; for example, we suspect that the directors in some cases actually function much as houseparents do in others. In any event, the full-time staff reported to us was as follows:

	Number of facilities	Number of staff
Houseparents	72	120
Directors	48	50
Clerical staff	24	34
Kitchen staff	24	42
Vocational/social counselors	23	29
Relief houseparents	20	23
LPN's, aides, attendants, "sub-professionals"	18	95
Social workers	17	23
Recreational, occupational, and activities therapists	10	14
Assistant directors	9	14
Registered nurses	7	13

	Number of facilities	Number of staff
Custodians	7	9
Coordinators	6	7
Students	6	23
Psychiatrists	2	2
Psychologists	1	2
Bus driver	1	1
Others	2	2

W E CAN SEE, AT THIS TIME, five appropriate uses for halfway houses for the mentally ill.

1. *To provide a setting and service that will "smooth the transition" back to the community for people who have been hospitalized.* This appears to have been the intention in creating most present halfway houses. In the mid- and late 1950's, as large numbers of state hospital patients began to be released back to communities that were substantially unprepared to provide the needed follow-up and support services, halfway houses began to be established as one means of filling the gap. The persuasions that long-hospitalized or "career" patients need help attaining or regaining the skills and capacities for coping with the exigencies of everyday life, plus a period of "phasing in" to community life, have a great deal of face validity. Even in the absence of very much definitive outcome data, it seems certain that halfway houses have helped a number of people to "make it" in community living. This will probably remain a major purpose of halfway houses.

2. The second purpose, already described, would be *as a more or less permanent placement* for people who no longer need to be in hospitals, do not require the physical care of nursing homes, yet have little potential to become employed or to live in the community without special supports. A good example of such a program is Cobble Hill Center, in Brooklyn (p. 89).

3. Closely related to both one and two, and somewhat overlapping, is the role of the halfway house in *reaching into the hospitals,* to recruit people who remain there because of the lack of an acceptable release plan. These may be people without families, or with families too chaotic or unwilling for the patient to return there.

4. A relatively new role is *as an alternative to hospitalization.* Some halfway houses evidence an interest in accepting people from the community who, but for the availability of the halfway house, would require hospitalization. Placement in a halfway house may be considerably less

alienating and disorganizing for the patient than admission to a psychiatric inpatient service. Almost inevitably, it would cost a great deal less. This can take the form of either a temporary refuge for the ex-resident who has a flare-up of disturbed behavior that calls for "tiding over," or as a definitive alternative for people already formally evaluated as requiring hospitalization.

One study has been completed of such use of the halfway house, and another is nearing completion. Under an NIMH grant, the Rehabilitation Mental Health Services in Santa Clara, California (p. 48), and Agnews State Hospital cooperated in a study in which patients needing hospitalization were randomly assigned to treatment either at the state hospital or at the Rehabilitation Mental Health Services' Community Care Home. "The results indicated that patients in the acute stages of psychiatric illness," says the final report, "could be treated effectively and within a shorter period of time in a residential community setting." The rehospitalization rate was higher for the state hospital group (37 percent) than for the Community Care Home group (29 percent).

> Within the Community Care Home group [the report continues] there was a more gradual but definite trend to reduced pathology, particularly of the types reflecting repression and withdrawal. Community Care Home patients appeared to become more active in dealing with their daily personal problems. There were no differences in employment status at admission; however, the Community Care Home group showed a greater achievement of employment and a larger income increase at discharge as compared with the Agnews State Hospital group.

The second study is the Spruce House Project of Philadelphia's Horizon House, also financed by an NIMH grant. The same random assignment of patients to the state hospital or to the halfway house characterizes this study, for which the data are still being processed.

5. Finally, we can see for halfway houses a large potential role as a facility that can serve *to shorten the length of inpatient stay.* This may sound much like some of the above-mentioned categories, but we have in mind something more specific. There are today many more people being treated for mental illness in short-term general hospital psychiatric units than in state hospitals. The average stay in these units as of 1963 was about 20 days[1] and there is some evidence that it has become shorter since then. We know of particular general hospital psychiatric units where the average stay is no more than a week.

---

[1] R. M. Glasscote and C. K. Kanno: *General Hospital Psychiatric Units: A National Survey.* Joint Information Service, Washington, D.C., 1965.

As the "crisis" treatment orientation spreads (as it seems to be), it should be feasible to build programs around the concept that the in-patient stay will be strictly limited to that period when the patient is so agitated as to require the protection that an inpatient service can afford, or so disorganized as to require heavier doses of medication than can safely be given outside a hospital. Experience indicates that for many patients this may be no more than three to four days. If a rather well-structured and suitably staffed halfway house were then available for transfer for an additional stay, the patient would be better served by getting into a more open and less alienating environment, and a great deal of money would be saved, since the cost of halfway house service, even when it has medical and other professional activities built in, is considerably less than the current costs of inpatient treatment in general hospitals.

What we are describing here is a concept that has often been proposed for the day hospital, and to some extent has been effectuated around the country.[2] However, in our 1968 study of day hospitals we estimated that the cost was likely to approach $20 per day. The halfway house, even in the face of inflation, will probably be able to provide a suitable "intermediate" service at less cost than the day hospital. Perhaps both day hospitals and halfway houses need to be encouraged to provide this particular role.

---

[2] R. M. Glasscote, A. M. Kraft, S. M. Glassman, and W. W. Jepson: *Partial Hospitalization for the Mentally Ill: A Study of Programs and Problems.* Joint Information Service, Washington, D.C., 1969.

V. Do Halfway Houses Work?

WALTER BARTON IN 1962[1] cautioned that

> No proof appears to be on record from past experience that the halfway house or its equivalent is worth the expense. . . . Tentative findings suggest that the number of patients who succeed and fail in the community after release from the mental hospital is not very much different if they go to a halfway house or to board in the community. About one third return to the hospital and two thirds remain out. . . .
>
> Further study will be needed to assess the value of a halfway facility. While its justification seems to rest on reasonable and logical grounds, someone has yet to perform a controlled study to determine whether release is accelerated, dependency diminished, or whether patient responsibility and sociability is enhanced when a transitional facility is used as compared with direct placement in the community.

WE HAVE MENTIONED THAT ONE CONTROLLED STUDY of a halfway house especially created to serve as an alternative to hospitalization has been completed and another is in process. But in respect of the primary intention of the vast majority of halfway houses, namely to prevent *re*hospitalization and to facilitate adjustment to autonomous and productive living in the community for those who have been hospitalized, the controlled study that Barton advocated has not been done.[2] The extent of the data collected by halfway houses, even those established as demonstrations, has been limited by and large to a follow-up only of those who resided in the houses.

It would be unreasonable to expect any halfway house to have a successful outcome with every one of its residents. For one thing, we know that the prognostic art simply does not permit anything close to such accurate selection. And if it did, a unanimously successful outcome might signify nothing more than an overly cautious and conservative

---

[1] W. E. Barton: *Administration in Psychiatry.* Charles C. Thomas, Springfield, Ill., 1962.

[2] Although one is in process at Mental Health Recovery, Inc., in Belmont, California, with results anticipated in 1972.

intake policy. Consequently, whether in simplest terms a halfway house "works" would have to be determined by *how much less often* the people it serves are rehospitalized than an equivalent group of people leaving hospitals who are not provided the services of a halfway house, and *how much more often* the halfway house residents are living autonomously and working.[3]

Outcome studies could, of course, be considerably more complex. One could involve not only the alternatives of "halfway house vs. no halfway house" but could also involve several halfway houses with different levels and kinds of staffing and expectations, placement directly into apartments, into foster homes, etc. But at minimum, it seems to us, some studies are needed that would include the following:

• Identification of individuals thought to be similar at least in the single dimension of seeming to need the supportive services of a halfway house. The criteria for needing the halfway house would have to be formally spelled out, and the assessment of each individual would need to be made jointly by the halfway house staff and the hospital staff responsible for discharge planning.

• Assignment by a random procedure of these individuals into two groups, one to be offered the halfway house service, the other not.

• Measurement of rehospitalization rate, employment rate, and living status at suitable intervals, such as each three months following discharge from hospital, for a maximum of perhaps three years. A longer follow-up period may be unsuitable, since by the end of three years one can assume that many other influences in addition to the halfway house experience will have come to have an effect on the individual's status.

Such a design would seem to require that the particular halfway house limit its intake to referrals from a single collaborating hospital. The numbers in the experimental and control groups would have to be large enough—we would think at absolute minimum fifty in each group—to allow some confidence in the results.

IN THE MEANTIME, we have little more to go on than the follow-up statistics that individual halfway houses have compiled. In our visits and our review of the literature, we found the lowest reported rehospitalization rate to be nine percent, the highest 45 percent. The basis for computation is not uniform; some include only those rehospitalized

---

[3] Roscoe House, p. 101, intended to use matched groups in such a study but had to call it off because of misconceptions that could not be dispelled among the referring personnel.

directly from the house, others include those rehospitalized at whatever time the follow-up was done—sometimes many months or a year later—and some include those who were only briefly rehospitalized, perhaps for no more than three or four days, and then readmitted to the halfway house.

One simply cannot know from data of this sort whether halfway houses "work." Even if a particular halfway house had a rehospitalization rate half that of the total population discharged from mental hospitals, this might reflect little more than the particular eligibility and screening procedures; conversely, even if the house had a rehospitalization rate twice that of the total group, it might still be "successful" if it were deliberately trying to select the most troubled and resourceless candidates.

P ERHAPS WHAT IS REALLY NEEDED is a study that will attempt to measure *the quality of life* of matched groups of ex-patients, one assigned to a halfway house, the other merely discharged to make whatever living arrangements they can. We do not think this is a sentimental approach; on the contrary, we think that there is an ever-rising level of expectations throughout society, one important aspect of which is whether life is "good" and whether it provides any sense of satisfaction, well-being, and self-fulfillment.

On the one hand, the mental health field points with satisfaction and a sense of accomplishment to a steadily dwindling census in state hospitals, signifying a dedication to the idea that it is better to be out of a state hospital than in one; on the other hand, the charge has frequently been made that state hospitals, in their eagerness to reduce their census, have sometimes discharged patients to inferior nursing homes, inadequate foster homes, and tiny single rooms in dilapidated residential hotels. Consequently, a perfectly valid basis on which to measure the effect of the halfway house, it seems to us, would be whether it provides an enhanced setting and opportunity for a better quality of life for the person who has been hospitalized for mental illness. Since relatively simple controlled studies of outcome in terms of residential and occupational status have not been completed, we wonder whether it is reasonable to expect that a "quality of life study" will be carried out. We think it should be.

In the meantime, our own persuasion, after visiting a variety of halfway houses, is that they offer a humane, compassionate, appropriate, warm, empathic environment which we believe is badly needed by a sizable number of people who leave state hospitals to try to acquire the skills and confidence they need to live and work in the community.

What we are saying, in the face of the lack of hard data, is that we believe the halfway house fits in extremely well with what we believe to have become a commitment to the mentally ill: not just the privilege but the right to live in the community, and to have as good a life there as possible. Research that will yield hard data should be undertaken. In the meantime, in a field that is notoriously short of hard data about many aspects of its services, we are willing with a good deal of "consensual conviction" to endorse the proliferation of halfway houses.

BEYOND THIS, ONE CAN ARGUE CONVINCINGLY for the halfway house on an economic basis. The cost of service varied greatly among the houses we visited, depending largely on how extensive their services were. In each case we attempted to assess the appropriateness of the expense by comparing it with the cost of retaining a person in the state hospital. This reflects our conclusions that a) the halfway houses were to a large extent serving seriously impaired people, many of whom might still need to be in the hospital but for the supportive services of the house and b) halfway houses could have an important future as alternatives to hospitalization. As a generalization, residence in a halfway house seemed to cost about half as much per day as in state hospitals, and a quarter or less of the cost in the psychiatric units of general hospitals.

ELEVEN PROGRAM DESCRIPTIONS

VI. Gutman Rehabilitation Programs, Inc. Portland, Oregon

F ROM ITS BEGINNINGS IN 1962 as a rehabilitation residence sponsored by the Mental Health Association of Oregon, Gutman House, following a period of support under a demonstration grant, became an incorporated independent agency. The residence later became one unit of a broader program when, in 1966, administrative offices were created and a halfway house for retarded men was added. In 1970 a halfway house for retarded women was added as the third component.

Origins

In tracing the history of Gutman House, it is difficult to discern the relative influence of several prior efforts in Oregon regarding rehabilitation of state hospital patients. The patient population of the (then two) state hospitals in Oregon peaked in the 1958-60 biennium and then began to decline; but even before the decline started, the hospitals had been involved with the state's Division of Vocational Rehabilitation, Department of Public Health, and Public Welfare Commission in a three-year demonstration and research project, largely funded by the federal rehabilitation program, to "provide a continuum of service between hospital and community, with follow-up services for the released mental patient being accomplished by county agencies." This involved placing vocational counselors in some of the treating facilities and the practice of sending discharge summaries from the state hospitals to the public health departments of the counties to which the discharged patients were returning.

At about the time this grant expired, the Joint Commission on Mental Illness and Health issued its report. The Mental Health Association of Oregon appointed committees to consider various aspects of the report, and one of these, concerned with rehabilitation, noted with alarm the increasing readmission rate to the state hospitals; as early as 1962, readmissions had climbed to 56 percent of all admissions. This situation posed questions for the rehabilitation committee.

> Could a follow-up service reduce the high readmission rate? If the hospital completed its treatment and returned the patient to the community, and the patient was then unable to sustain himself there, is this a failure on the part of the community to help the patient during the difficult transition phase from hospital to "normal living"?

The board of the mental health association assigned to the rehabilitation committee the task of determining what kind of follow-up services would be most helpful to ex-patients. An influence in this process was the report of mental health association staff members who had made visits to several halfway houses in the East. Also having its influence was the report of an earlier survey made by the Oregon chapter of the National Rehabilitation Association, which revealed that little or no attention was given to the ex-patient after his discharge from the mental hospital.

> A critical finding was that many patients returned to their homes or to family life, but few were able either to seek or find employment. Another finding was that many patients suffered a relapse seemingly because of inadequate medication, or because they were living in a situation not conducive to their continued emotional well-being. The information provided the insight that a number of former mental patients probably need a supervised, wholesome living situation, particularly during the first few months after hospitalization.

The rehabilitation committee gave first priorities to the problems of finding employment and, for those who did not have suitable families, a supportive transitional living arrangement. It proposed that the mental health association, collaborating with appropriate public agencies, sponsor a rehabilitation residence, which would provide both the specialized residential environment and the guidance and support that ex-patients were believed to need in locating jobs. The board approved. An application for a demonstration grant was submitted to and approved by the Social and Rehabilitation Service, and the project began in mid-1962. A steering committee of the mental health association was appointed to oversee the new program which, following a lengthy search, was established in a large former private home. The first residents came late in 1962. In 1963 the facility was named the Eleanor B. Gutman Rehabilitation House, honoring the memory of a psychiatrist who over a long career had taken particular interest in the plight of mental patients after they leave the hospital.

The rehabilitation house sought to provide not only a homelike living situation but also social and recreational activities, vocational guidance, training, and placement, and "continuous encouragement and moral support supplied both by staff and fellow residents." Despite emphasis on a "normal living" situation, the program recognized the need to allow for "occasional lapses into dependency without the danger of rehospitalization that might accrue to the patient living alone in the community."

The program stated the goals of the three-year demonstration project as follows:

- To increase substantially the number of mentally handicapped persons capable of remaining in the community in remunerative employment.

- To strengthen and increase state and community resources for the rehabilitation of mentally disabled persons, particularly those patients who have not been helped by existing facilities and traditional methods.

- To make immediate application of new knowledge, methods, and techniques acquired through operation of other demonstration projects in recent years.

- To combine the resources of voluntary organizations with public services in a dynamic program to obtain these objectives.

- To confirm and further demonstrate the effectiveness of the rehabilitation house as a particular type of therapeutic intervention in the treatment and rehabilitation of the mentally ill.

- To improve and extend techniques for the reorientation, social adaptation, and personal and vocational adjustment of the mentally ill, and to contribute to increased rehabilitation efforts for this group of persons.

- To compare "successful" and "unsuccessful" patients who have been residents of the rehabilitation house, in an effort to define criteria which may guide agencies serving former residents of mental hospitals.

- To help dispel ignorance and misunderstanding of mental illness by the community, and to demonstrate to employers that recovered mental patients are valuable employees.

Physical facilities

Gutman House was established in a residential section of Portland, convenient to public transportation and readily accessible to the business district. It is a three-story frame building on a large, pleasantly landscaped corner lot. The neighborhood is middle class, comprised mainly of large, attractive, well-maintained homes, many of which are still private residences, some of which have become boarding and rooming houses. There are some attractive smaller apartment buildings.

The first floor of the house consists of a very large living room; a large dining room, which is more than ample for the twelve residents to have their meals together; a large, well-equipped kitchen; a breakfast room; and a small parlor used by the staff for counseling residents.

The second floor is used for the five men. There are one single and two double bedrooms, plus an additional bedroom used by the house managers. The third floor, where the seven women live, has a similar layout, with one single and three double bedrooms. The front stairs are used only by the men, the back stairs only by the women, thus preserving privacy for the sleeping areas of the house.

The house is clean, well furnished, and comfortable. It has a gracious yet informal air about it. Its attributes are a particularly conscious part of the program's philosophy.

> A rehabilitation house [should] be located in a middle-class residential area. . . . Location in a wealthy district might result in too many invidious comparisons of the residents with the property owners. On the other hand, location in an area with low standards of living must be guarded against. Clients often need the uplift of morale that comes from pleasant living conditions, and a depressing living situation might have an adverse effect upon social adjustment. Many residents expressed the feeling that this is the only real home they have ever had, and want to feel proud of it.

The house was initially leased; in 1966 it was purchased, with a twelve-year mortgage.

The staff

The administrative office that oversees Gutman House and the two halfway houses for retardates is staffed by an executive director, a job placement specialist, a social worker, an administrative assistant, and a full-time plus a part-time secretary. All are involved in the operations of all three houses, the amount of time devoted to each varying with circumstances. Gutman House seems to receive a bit more than a third of staff time, since its residents present a larger variety of problems than do the retardates.

The executive director, Arthur Newman, is an all-pervasive influence in the program. An Englishman who had worked in English rehabilitation programs as a vocational specialist, he came to Oregon in the early 1960's to retire. Gutman House was concurrently completing its first year of operation, which was a considerable disappointment; of thirteen residents who came to live there shortly after it opened, nine had returned to hospital and the other four had accomplished little in the way of finding and keeping jobs. Charles Feike, who at one time headed up the state's vocational rehabilitation program and had since become director of the mental health association, at that time still the principal sponsor of Gutman House, was acquainted with Mr. Newman from earlier times. He prevailed upon him to accept a job as placement specialist. He did so. Later, when the position of executive director was created, he moved into that new slot.

An action-oriented man of very positive personality, he seems confident that he knows what is best for Gutman House clients. He is entirely dedicated to the British philosophy of mental illness, as part of which work itself is endowed with great therapeutic value, taking priority over every other aspect of rehabilitation. He set about as soon as he was on the job to identify employers who would give an opportunity to people with a history of mental illness. Within a short time the program had accomplished a remarkable turnaround.

Mr. Newman pursues the philosophy that no resident must be allowed to sit idle and that a pay check is among the most therapeutic devices available. People who have been long-term patients in mental hospitals, he believes, often do better in jobs on a lower scale than that which they may personally prefer or seem to have the background or potentiality for. Put another way, he believes that a major reason for the relapse of ex-patients is their attempting to perform jobs that make demands on them which create stress and eventuate in a breakdown precipitating rehospitalization.

The social worker, with a bachelor's degree, had come to the program two years earlier from Goodwill Industries. She spends about a third of her time at the administrative offices and divides the rest among the three halfway houses, spending proportionately more time at Gutman House, where she is present an average of two hours a day including two evenings a week. She handles inquiries from referral sources, participates in the intake procedure, helps to work out the applicant's financial eligibility, interviews relatives, develops a plan for medication follow-up, provides backup and support for the house managers, and sees all of the residents, some informally and on request, a few regularly in scheduled appointments. She seemed to operate in appropriate ways on a practical, common-sense level.

The job placement specialist recruits jobs, taking special pains to acquaint the prospective employer with any problems he thinks a particular candidate might present. If it seems necessary he rides the bus with the resident to his new job, then meets him after work to accompany him to the halfway house. He stays in regular touch with each employer, sometimes by telephone, sometimes by visits. He holds scheduled sessions with each employee. And he attends the evening group meetings of the halfway house residents.

The only personnel assigned exclusively to Gutman House are the house managers, a couple who live on the premises during the five days a week they are on duty and then repair to their own living quarters for their days off, and a relief house manager who covers on the two days a week that the house managers are away.

We did not talk with the house managers, who had been hired quite recently, but instead spent our time with the relief house manager, who until recently had been the full-time house manager. With a background as a practical nurse, she came to Gutman House from a job as housemother at a home for delinquent girls. She learned of Gutman House through a classified advertisement and accepted the job because it seemed both interesting and worthwhile. She said that she and her husband had found more odd behavior among the residents than they had expected. She felt that their main problems had been in dealing with residents who became withdrawn or who failed to take their medications. To support those who were having trouble, she and her husband mobilized fellow residents, and when this did not work, intervened themselves. Only if these attempts failed did they turn for professional help, either to the social worker or to Mr. Newman; this was rarely necessary, perhaps on the average less than once per week. She and her husband had left the job as full-time house managers because her husband had reached retirement age and also because "the work gets to you after a while."

The sole remaining member of the staff spends little time in the program but obviously wields major influence and is felt to make a major contribution. He is Dr. George Saslow, psychiatric consultant to the entire program but with particular emphasis on Gutman House. Director of the psychiatric residency program at the University of Oregon Medical School, Dr. Saslow impressed us as a man of extraordinary erudition, with a deep commitment to research in new approaches to serving the mentally ill, and attuned to the changes and enhanced opportunities that have come about in recent years. On the average he devotes six to eight hours a month or less to the program, but he is on call for emergencies at all times. He regularly attends the weekly staff meetings, oversees medication for the residents, and often participates in the intake and evaluation activities.

The residents

Gutman House, at the time it began operating and for some years afterward, identified as its target population the long-hospitalized chronic schizophrenic patient.

Until shortly before the house opened, all mental patients from Portland were served by Oregon State Hospital, in Salem. In 1961 a smaller acute-treatment psychiatric hospital, the 450-bed Dammasch State Hospital, opened about twenty miles from Portland, and since then it has been responsible for treating patients from the county in which Portland is located and two adjacent counties. However, the largest residual population fitting the Gutman House purpose was that which had accumulated at Oregon State Hospital, and in those early years there were more residents from Salem than from the new, nearby hospital. During the three years of support under the demonstration grant there were 82 residents, whose mean length of hospitalization was 5.4 years. The average age was 38 years.

As the characteristics of the state hospital patients have changed over the years, so have the characteristics of the Gutman House residents. After a number of the suitable candidates from Oregon State Hospital had been accepted, referrals from that hospital declined somewhat, while referrals from Dammasch increased. The average age of the residents has dropped to about 35, and there are now more residents with a shorter history of illness. Among 44 persons who resided in the house during 1969, 70 percent were under 40. Specifically, 12 percent were under 21; 35 percent were between 21 and 30; 23 percent were between 31 and 40; 14 percent were between 41 and 50; 12 percent were between 51 and 60; and five percent were over 60.

Mr. Newman states that there has come to be less emphasis on diagnosis, not because there are fewer schizophrenics but because experience indicated that diagnosis was not very predictive of who would do well in the program. While schizophrenics still constitute the majority, the number of persons with recurring depressions has increased. Gutman House believes that behavioral characteristics are more informative than diagnosis.

The house sets no formal limit on stay but hopes to have residents working and relocated in an autonomous community living arrangement within six months. In 1969, 25 percent of the men and 46 percent of the women stayed less than a month; this group represents both some early successes and some who faltered early and had to leave the program to return to the hospital. Thirty-five percent of the men and 33 percent of the women stayed between one and three months; 25 percent of the men and 13 percent of the women stayed between four and six months; 15 percent of the men and eight percent of the women stayed between six months and a year; and no one stayed longer than a year.

The house has also somewhat relaxed its original age limits, which were designated as 18 to 60. It will not, however, take anyone under the age of 16, since this is the legal minimum age for accepting employment in Oregon. Candidates over 60 are now freely accepted, provided they seem to have a clear vocational potential.

During our visit we interviewed three of the current residents, all of whom seemed to exemplify the dilemma of the selection process, namely, to recruit residents who have high motivation to become employed and to live autonomously in the community, but who at the same time are handicapped from doing so by a variety of serious problems. We were impressed that the program seemed to be succeeding with a depressed woman who was epileptic, had heart trouble, had attempted suicide, was separated from her husband, and had been forced to place her several children in foster homes. Within a week of her arrival she had been placed in a job, and in our interview she was talking of her plans in the near future to move to her own apartment and take her children back. A young man with some college education but with a history of numerous hospitalizations over a six-year period was working full time as a dishwasher and part time as a waiter, and he seemed to be having more success with this low-demand work than he had had in several previous jobs.

The program

Gutman House seeks to enable its residents to live autonomously in the community while successfully engaged in compensated, competitive work. Says a report issued by the program:

> . . . social and vocational rehabilitation [are not] two easily distinguishable aspects of the total Gutman House program. . . . Successful rehabilitation of necessity requires both aspects, particularly in the case of the former mental patient whose attitudes toward and relationships with others may be impaired.

What the desired outcome consists of in terms of modification of particular behaviors, attitudes, and capabilities is spelled out in a description of the progress ideally hoped for in each resident.

1. *Self-care:* from poorly dressed, poorly groomed, and showing a lack of interest in one's personal appearance to a point where the resident purchases, pays for, and maintains his own wardrobe and cares for his personal grooming with no supervision.

2. *Home surroundings:* from lack of concern with one's surroundings to responsibility for the care and orderliness of one's own room and personal belongings.

3. *Travel:* from participation in escorted tours of the city to complete responsibility for one's own coming and going around the city, including getting to and from the job.

4. *Social:* from participation only in house-sponsored social affairs with other residents to making one's own social and recreational contacts in the general community.

5. *Vocational:* from carrying out assigned chores around the house to a full-time job in competitive employment.

6. *Financial:* from control of personal funds by rehabilitation house staff to complete financial independence.

7. *Emotional:* from the withdrawal, suspicion, and emotional flatness characteristic of the schizophrenic to more confident, friendly attitudes characteristic of the mature adult.

Mr. Newman is not convinced that all mental hospital patients can be rehabilitated; indeed, quite the reverse, resulting in important selection criteria. The poor outcome of the first year of the program was felt to have stemmed entirely from the failure to select residents appropriately. Says a report of those early years:

> Gutman House staff had in mind that a hospital screening committee composed of the physician, the social worker, the nurse, the psychiatric aide, and others—such as a rehabilitation counselor or an occupational therapist, if available—would participate in making up a written report about each patient who was being referred. . . . After the first few months, it became evident that the screening reports were written by only one or two individuals, not always the person who knew the patient best. In some instances, major characteristics of the patient, such as physical disabilities, alcoholism, or homosexual behavior were not mentioned. Such omissions were not discovered until the client had taken up residence at Gutman House. Often, he had to be returned to hospital within a few days or a few weeks.

"The hospitals were anxious to see whether we could perform miracles with some of their most hopeless cases," Mr. Newman told us. After the first year, Gutman House staff began to take a more active part in the screening. The newly hired vocational specialist and the social worker met at each hospital with the hospital committee, where they interviewed each applicant. Later on, the hospital began the practice of submitting a comprehensive narrative report on each candidate prior to the visit of the Gutman House staff.

The practice of the Gutman House professionals—now the executive director, social worker, and job placement specialist—going to the hospital to interview prospective clients continues up to the present time. At this interview, they make clear what will be expected of the applicant and what he will get in return. They assure him that they can and will get a job for him, but in many cases indicate their belief that he should start at a lower-level job than he has anticipated. They explore what precipitated his hospitalization, in the hope thereby that such conditions may be avoided in the future.

Gutman House will not accept alcoholics, drug users, sex deviates, or people with physical handicaps that would preclude employment. About seventy percent of the people referred to them by the hospitals are accepted. Whether the candidate wants to come is one of the matters most specifically pursued, and if he does not, he is dropped from consideration.

The decision whether to accept the candidate is usually made at the time of this visit to the hospital. If the decision is favorable, arrangements must be made for his acceptance as a Vocational Rehabilitation client, if this seems suitable or necessary, or, in other cases, for a financial plan that will provide the money to pay for his room and board at Gutman House. The procedure may involve several weeks in a particular case but is usually completed within two weeks.

The prospective member does not pay a "trial visit," on the grounds that Gutman House is the home of the people already living there and that it is not fair to them to impose visits from strangers.

When the new resident arrives, the house managers take him in hand to teach him the layout of the house and to remind him of the rules. "The friendly reception provided by the house managers may spell the difference between a receptive and an uncooperative attitude on the part of the patient who is entering a new life after a long hospital stay," says a Gutman House report. In some cases a volunteer takes the new resident on a tour of the city to orient him (although many Gutman House residents previously lived in Portland, some have been hospitalized so long that the city has changed and is thus unfamiliar to them). Transportation facilities, theaters, parks, and recreational facilities are pointed out.

Throughout the orientation period "care is taken by staff members to be continuously supportive and encouraging" but at the same time firm, in the hope that "all patients will realize that this is a place for them to take over increasing responsibility for themselves, and that they are expected to observe house rules designed to make group living easier for all."

Residents are expected to maintain their own rooms and handle their own laundry. A variety of more general household chores, such as helping to prepare meals, to clean up afterward, and caring for the grounds, are assigned by consensus of the residents and the house managers. If a resident is awaiting employment, he is expected to take a larger load of the household duties. In general, this has been no problem, and, in fact, several former residents who have moved to private living quarters in the vicinity come back occasionally on weekends and days off to help with cleaning.

The social worker must often help the residents budget their money. Those who have been in hospital a long time are particularly inept; in extreme cases their checks are held by the house until a plan for the money has been formulated with the social worker.

IN THE VIEW OF GUTMAN HOUSE, the single most useful technique for maintaining oneself in the community is work. Analysis of psychological and social deficits and efforts to improve psychological and social skills take place in the context of the work experience.

Dr. Saslow described the Gutman House concept of the role of work.

> We have the viewpoint that work competence is a different kind of competence which requires special attention and can be, in and of itself, tremendously rehabilitative and therapeutic, without raising other kinds of problems. . . . In our early years, we observed that the personnel in the hospitals from which we received our referrals—the social workers, the psychologists, and the psychiatrists—operated on the notion that a person could develop better work competence if he worked out earlier life problems. In this program we have specifically rejected this well-known dogma. We also found that the vocational rehabilitation counselors on whom we necessarily relied also believed that unless a person had worked out personality problems in counseling fashion, he was not ready for work. I made my own view known to the staff: work competence is not something that can be generalized from other kinds of capabilities.

Mr. Newman reported that over the years he had contacted more than six hundred employers in order to line up jobs for Gutman House clients.

> I get the jobs, first of all, by keeping in close touch with the state employment office. I also read the classified ads very carefully. Other sources of supply are the chamber of commerce newspaper, and any of the industrial papers that describe business expansions. If I find a firm is expanding, from my past industrial experience I have a fairly good idea what sort of unskilled labor they will need; so I get in touch with the personnel manager, making personal friends with him. . . . I always tell the resident, before I take him to the job, that I am going to inform the employer about the illness. I don't go into gory details, but I do make sure that the employer knows this man has had a mental problem and what the employer should look out for.

Very few employers have refused to accept Gutman House residents; on the contrary, there have usually been more jobs available than residents to fill them. At the time of our visit to Gutman House, all of the residents were working except one woman who was thought not quite ready. Small industries, restaurants, private clubs, and farms offer the greatest number of openings. Mr. Newman feels that a good knowledge of the needs of industry is important to successful placement of the mentally ill. "People in industry don't engage clients through sympathy; they expect production," he said.

Much of the staff effort is directed toward the resident's work experience. The resident is ordinarily accompanied by a staff member when he goes for his job interview. Problems on the job occupy a good part of the weekly meeting of the residents with the professional staff. The vocational specialist sees residents as needed concerning their work adjustment. A number of the problems brought to the social worker and the house managers concern things that have arisen on the job.

Ability to function on the job is the foremost determinant of when the resident is prepared to move on to some more autonomous living arrangement. However, those who do so are maintained for as long as seems necessary in the caseload of the professional staff, and former residents of Gutman House are welcome to return to the weekly residents' meeting.

There is relatively little planned program within the house. "Over the years," Mr. Newman told us, "we found that regularly organized social activities were not well attended. For one reason we have a regularly changing population, and for another there is a considerable range of age among our residents, with attendant differences in their likes and dislikes." Since a number of residents formerly lived in Portland, many leave the house to spend time with relatives. A small group of women volunteers does, however, organize various special events, such as picnics, birthday parties, and holiday parties, which are usually well attended. Free tickets are often available for local theater and sports events.

Medication and medical service

Gutman House places great emphasis on evaluating each client's need for psychotropic medications. Early in the program, a report states, "the extreme importance of medication" was not adequately realized. But within the first few months the staff discovered that residents often decided to experiment with medication, some of them taking different dosages for several days before the staff became aware of it, others stopping medication entirely. "Virtually all of the failures, those who had to return to the hospital," the report says, "were caused by discontinuance of the daily doses of tranquilizing or energizing drugs."

A precondition for acceptance by Gutman House is the patient's ability to supervise his own medication. Each client coming from the state hospital is expected to bring with him a reasonable supply, plus a prescription. Thereafter, Dr. Saslow takes over medication responsibility for substantially all residents. Every other week he reviews each resident's medication, changes the dosage or the type as seems indicated, and provides further prescriptions. Frequently he reduces the amount, sometimes because the dosages prescribed by the hospital seem too strong, in other cases because of evident gains from the support of the halfway house and successful experience on the job. He told us that he is "very much concerned about the hazards to patients when there's more than one drug, when the drugs are continued too long, and when the dosages are high."

Some residents qualify for money for medication from the welfare department. Those who are Vocational Rehabilitation clients have their medication paid for as part of their training program. Those who are working and have the means pay for their own drugs. Gutman House pays for drugs from its own funds for the occasional resident who does not fall into any of these categories.

A resident who moves from the house to private living arrangements and does not have the income to pay for drugs is referred to the mental health clinic of the county department of public health, to the medical school outpatient department, or to some other public or private health or medical agency. In particular cases, however, Dr. Saslow continues to oversee medication of former residents. Not infrequently he resumes medication responsibility for a former resident who is concerned about the medication prescribed for him by an outside agency.

Gutman House is inclined to see the need for medication for many of its clients as long-term, perhaps permanent. Says one of its reports:

> . . . part of the resocializing experience [should] be an emphasis upon the necessity to maintain the medication regimen, for life, if necessary. This emphasis should be begun early in the client's residence and continued throughout the follow-up period. In some instances a physician may be needed to reiterate to the client that the tranquilizing drugs are necessary for the continuance of his good emotional health, that they are not habit-forming, that they will not injure him in other ways. It is of course virtually impossible to overcome entrenched values, such as an objection to drugs on religious grounds. Such clients may never achieve complete rehabilitation.

Outcome

Once the difficulties of the first year had been overcome, the Gutman House program accomplished a rehabilitation record for its clients that has been fairly steadily maintained over the years. Results with the residents are calculated according to three categories: a) failures, who return to hospital; b) residents who move on to some autonomous living arrangement in the community but are supported by welfare or otherwise are not working; c) residents who take up private living arrangements and are working either in a sheltered setting or in competitive employment. For purposes of statistical reporting within the requirements of the state Vocational Rehabilitation agency, those in category b) are not considered successful rehabilitations; Gutman House believes they should be considered successful, in that one should be considered better off living in the community, even if unproductively, than living in a state hospital.

During the three years of the SRS demonstration grant, slightly more than half of the residents were successfully rehabilitated by the criterion that a follow-up made ninety days after their departure from Gutman House found them living autonomously and working.

These figures were substantially the same for the period of the most recent annual report (the year ending October 1969). During that year 38 residents left the house; 20, or 53 percent, represented successful rehabilitations; nine, or 24 percent, were living in the community but not employed; another nine were returned to hospital.

Length of hospitalization does not seem to be a factor in outcome. Successful rehabilitation has been accomplished both with briefly hospitalized and long-term patients. Length of residence in Gutman House does not vary between those who work and do not work while living autonomously in the community, but the stay is considerably shorter for most of those who return to hospital, signifying that when "failure" is to be the outcome it is usually manifest within the first month or two.

On the face of it, even considering that Gutman House rejects about thirty percent of the applicants referred to it, this seems an impressive outcome. One must keep in mind, however, that the statistics have been limited to a ninety-day follow-up, and consequently it is not known how many have subsequently relapsed and required rehospitalization. If one could assume (as of course one cannot) that all of the successful rehabilitations were people who continued to live and work in the community, then one could, in financial terms alone, calculate that Gutman House has saved literally millions of dollars in public funds. Despite the well-known difficulties of following up mental patients after any considerable period of time, it would be extremely useful if a longitudinal follow-up were done of all those who were successfully rehabilitated in Gutman House.

An interesting aspect of the most recent annual report is the evident continued difficulty in educating the referring hospitals to the target population. Of 42 applicants referred, the house turned down 12. One of these was a man "who had no hesitation in stating during the initial interview that he had no inclination at all to be employed." Another was a professional woman with a long-standing history of addiction to major drugs of abuse and a record of failure with numerous other agencies. Several were found to be on such heavy dosages of medication that it was considered inadvisable to accept them.

It seems worth repeating here that, during the three years of the demonstration grant, in every case when a resident had to return to hospital this outcome was attributed to his failure to follow the prescribed medication regimen.

Agency and community relationships

Gutman House seems to be highly regarded by the various agencies that it deals with and well supported by the surrounding neighborhood.

The regional director for mental illness clients of the Division of Vocational Rehabilitation expressed his agency's satisfaction with the outcome for its clients who have resided at Gutman House under DVR sponsorship. Although there are not always sufficient funds to meet all the applications for Vocational Rehabilitation training and sponsorship in Oregon, Gutman House is an agency whose clients are accommodated in all possible cases.

Relationships with the medical and psychiatric community appear to be of high quality, in large measure we suspect because of the program's relationship with Dr. Saslow. Gutman House clients can readily obtain service in emergencies from the clinical facilities of the medical school.

Relationships with the neighbors have been particularly favorable. Shortly before the first residents moved in, staff and volunteers paid a call on all neighbors within two blocks, explaining the purpose and inviting them to an open house. More than twenty percent of all the neighbors attended. They have been consistently supportive. Gutman House strongly recommends to any new halfway house that it plan such an educational effort with the neighbors. (This experience is, however, as other program descriptions indicate, strongly in contrast with that of some other halfway houses.)

Relatively few residents have been judged to require sheltered work placements, but these occasional referrals have been readily accepted by Goodwill Industries and the St. Vincent de Paul Society.

The house is subject to a variety of local regulations. The public health department requires that all residents, since they take turns helping out in the kitchen, have chest X rays and attend a two-hour lecture on food handling. The fire marshal prohibits smoking except on the first floor. Gutman House is licensed by the city as a tavern; there was no classification covering halfway houses, and of various poor fits, the category of tavern seemed to come closest.

Financing

The complete Gutman rehabilitation program, including all three halfway houses, operated in fiscal 1970 on a budget of about $137,000. Slightly less than half of this consisted of state funds made available through the Multnomah County mental health division, under the provisions of the state community mental health act. Thirty-three percent of the budget represents support from the Division of Vocational Rehabilitation on a purchase-of-service basis. Nineteen percent represents residents' payments for room and board. Only about one percent comes from other sources.

The Division of Vocational Rehabilitation for some years paid Gutman House $75 per month per resident for services under the provisions of a Personal Adjustment Training program. At the time of our visit the arrangement was being revised; Dr. Saslow, formerly paid directly by Vocational Rehabilitation, was in process of coming onto the Gutman House payroll, and the position of vocational specialist was also to be covered directly by Gutman House. As a result Vocational Rehabilitation had agreed to increase the fee to $150 per resident per month, with Gutman House staff directly providing psychiatric supervision and vocational placement.

Each resident is charged $90 per month for room and board. Those who are working pay this from their earnings. Most of those who are not working receive money from welfare, which also allows an additional $16 per month for incidental personal expenses.

As best can be calculated, the cost of maintaining a resident in Gutman House is approximately $12 per day, including all services. This sum is about the same as the per diem expenditure at Oregon State Hospital and about half the per diem expenditure at Dammasch State Hospital. Thus, on a purely economic basis, the program represents a saving of public money, even without taking into account the income earned by the Gutman House residents. Beyond this, of course, are the benefits that accrue to the residents by their living in the community rather than in a state hospital.

VII. Rehabilitation Mental Health Services, Inc. Santa Clara, California

F ROM A MODEST BEGINNING IN 1956, when it opened a small halfway house for men, Rehabilitation Mental Health Services has expanded to a network of community residential facilities that includes a halfway house for women, a facility designed to serve the acutely ill psychiatric patient who would otherwise require hospitalization, a residence for disturbed and delinquent adolescent boys, and a residence-workshop for chronically ill low-functioning men. This ambitious program approaches a new model for serving the mentally ill in the community.

Origins

Rehabilitation Mental Health Services (RMHS) traces its origins to 1953, when a group of private citizens came into contact with one another around their concern for the needs of people being discharged from nearby Agnews State Hospital. Dr. Walter Rappaport, who at that time was superintendent of Agnews, invited community leaders, including representatives of industry, business, and labor, to discuss the plight of patients leaving the hospital without funds, family, or employment. From these initial meetings grew a citizens group which established its primary goals as finding housing and employment for patients leaving the hospital and the education of the community regarding transitional problems encountered by patients. A volunteer service was developed at the hospital, composed of two committees, a Volunteer Services Committee working with inpatients, and the Rehabilitation Planning Committee, working with patients following discharge. The Rehabilitation Planning Committee became incorporated in 1960 and later severed its legal ties with the hospital's Volunteer Services Committee and changed its name to Rehabilitation Mental Health Services. In doing so it maintained the "citizens" character of the group and community orientation and its cooperative relationship with the hospital.

During its first three years the Rehabilitation Planning Committee devoted itself primarily to helping to locate private residential placements and providing vocational counseling and finding jobs for the former patients. With time, the need was felt for a supervised residential facility. In 1956 a grant request was submitted to the federal Social and Rehabilitation Service, asking support for a demonstration halfway house for men. Later that year, the Quarters for Men was opened, accommodating seven residents. It was one of the first halfway houses in the United States.

At the expiration of the grant in 1959, the organization nearly became bankrupt. With a great deal of struggling for temporary funds and with some support from the Santa Clara County Association for Mental Health, it survived the following year and then, in 1960, was approved for funding under the state Short-Doyle (community mental health act) program. The small agency soon became stabilized, then began to expand; since that time the Short-Doyle funds have continued to be the major source of revenue.

In 1961, in nearby San Jose, a second halfway house, the Quarters for Women, was opened, accommodating nine residents. In 1964 a four-year National Institute of Mental Health research grant was awarded to establish a "Community Care Home" that would serve as an alternate to hospitalization for mentally ill people already evaluated as requiring 24-hour care. In early 1969, with the aid of a staffing grant from NIMH, the Adolescent Residential Center, consisting of two residential facilities, was opened for adolescent boys, most of whom have had both emotional problems requiring specialized service and a history of trouble with juvenile authorities. As the most recent component, the Residence-Workshop program was established in October 1969, with funds from the county Short-Doyle program, United Fund, and the Santa Clara County Association for Mental Health, to provide residence to twelve long-hospitalized men and workshop facilities for these men with a plan for others who come to the workshop from other living arrangements in the community.

The staff

RMHS has a staff of seventeen persons, including administrative and clerical employees. Overseeing the several residential facilities is an administrative office staff consisting of the program's executive director, a business and office manager, a bookkeeper, and three clerk-typists.

Each of the residential programs has a "facility supervisor," who, in a considerably autonomous fashion, oversees the activities of his particular program and develops and implements a treatment and rehabilitation program for each resident. Reporting to the facility supervisor at each program is a full-time residence manager and a relief manager. This simple and consistent pattern accounts for the entire staff, except for a workshop manager who supervises the daytime activities of the sheltered workshop, a two-thirds-time psychiatrist who assumes medical responsibility for all the residents, and a client counselor in the adolescent program who leads group programs, develops and participates in activity programs, and counsels residents individually.

The executive director, Leonard H. Goveia, has a master's degree in psychology. He came to the program in 1958, during the third year of the SRS demonstration grant that funded the agency's first residence. While completing his graduate work he was working nights at Agnews State Hospital, where he learned of the Quarters for Men and was asked, when a vacancy occurred, if he would be interested in a job. A few months later the rest of the staff members left, the grant expired, and Mr. Goveia was the sole employee to weather the perilous financial year of 1959. An articulate, soft-spoken man, he clearly has extraordinary capabilities to relate successfully to various agencies whose support is needed by RMHS, obtaining and maintaining sources of support for the continuing program and for expansion into new directions.

A most deliberate feature of the staffing of this agency has been the practice of engaging employees who, on the one hand, appear to have the personal characteristics and assets that are helpful in dealing with people who have a history of mental illness, but at the same time are trained at the lowest level consistent with the kinds of responsibilities and duties they must carry. The only person in this program trained at the doctoral level is the psychiatrist, whose activities are described below. Of the facility supervisors, one has a bachelor's degree in sociology. Another, a registered nurse, was completing her work for a master's degree in sociology. Another has a master's degree in psychology. The fourth has three years of college work but no degree. All have had a variety of relevant previous job experiences; for example, the supervisor of the Residence-Workshop had worked as a vocational counselor and as a staff member of correctional halfway houses.

These supervisors develop and implement program and train, supervise, and support facility staff, take turns on weekend call, have scheduled and unscheduled counseling sessions with the residents, lead group therapy meetings, attend other house and agency meetings, and work with a variety of outside agencies to coordinate programs for the individual residents.

It is of course not uncommon these days for mental health programs to invest considerable responsibility in people who are trained at the bachelor's and master's level. Perhaps this practice of RMHS seemed so remarkable to us because it is openly attributed to a conviction that it is undesirable to have the most highly trained category of staff in such a program. The director said that the agency is fearful that it "would contaminate the program" if more highly trained personnel were introduced, and this persuasion was echoed by the psychiatrist and by the two board members whom we interviewed.

The attitude, in retrospect, seems to be part of an antiprofessional sentiment that is pronounced in many of the mental health facilities that we have visited in the past several years. This intricate and complex phenomenon is outside the scope of this study of halfway houses, but it is important to acknowledge. Contributing to it appear to be *a*) a dissatisfaction with the outcome of historic professional interventions with the mentally ill; *b*) a concern that prolonged training in the mental health disciplines inculcates so profound an emphasis on pathology as to limit the professional's capacity to recognize and work with the healthy aspects of the patient; *c*) reverberations of a questioning of the whole idea of formal training that abounds in colleges all over the country; and *d*) an almost defiant assertion that "good" and "positive" personal characteristics are so much more important than professional training as to render the training superfluous and irrelevant. Obviously a related manifestation is the fairly widespread conviction of recent years that "indigenous" personnel should be brought into mental health programs not merely to relieve trained personnel of low-level tasks but because of positive contributions they can make.

An argument that suggests itself here is that the person who has earned a master's or even a bachelor's degree in a behavioral or social science has had from four to six years of "higher" education and is not, after all, so minimally trained. In any event, at RMHS these less-than-doctoral-level staff members appeared to be functioning well. Each impressed us as highly motivated, competent, articulate, well informed, and deeply invested in the program. Only one, the supervisor who had completed only three years of college work, felt uncomfortable about his competence; he seemed to be convinced that with more training he would be able to carry out his present responsibilities in substantially less time than they now take.

Seemingly a source of pride to the agency is the fact that it successfully utilizes staff in positions that they could not qualify for in official public agencies. Said the president of the board:

> Having been in the state civil service system, I've seen the inadequacies of its rigid approach. I've seen many highly competent people who

couldn't move ahead because they didn't meet the particular criteria of the personnel department.

The residence managers had been with the program for periods ranging from a few weeks to four years. None has more than a high school diploma. All seemed to be pleasant, warm, easygoing women who were extremely involved in their work. In addition to their responsibilities of overseeing the housework and planning menus, shopping for food, and cooking dinner, they associate as in any home with the residents, and in many cases discuss the residents' problems with them. They are expected to enhance the residents' capabilities at cooking, shopping, grooming, and social interaction. They participate as members of the team involved with intake, program planning, and discharge planning for each resident.

A remarkable member of the staff is Dr. Emmett B. Litteral, the psychiatrist, who is involved in intake evaluation, staff consultation, and crisis intervention. For some years the assistant superintendent of Agnews State Hospital, he is now technically retired but in fact works about five hours a day in the RMHS program. He accepts psychiatric and for the most part medical responsibility for the 54 residents in the various programs. Beyond this, he lends the authority of his medical degree in a manner that legitimates the agency with some of the more traditional agencies that it must deal with. While not required to, Dr. Litteral does physical evaluations within the limits of the facilities at his disposal on all admissions to the Community Care Home. For all the residents, he acts as house physician in routine illnesses, although when more serious disease is involved the resident is referred to an outside specialist who may hospitalize him at a local hospital.

Dr. Litteral also has a large following of former residents who have moved on to independent living arrangements but who return periodically for prescriptions and consultation. He does not mind providing this service, particularly because he has found through the years that many patients, when referred to another agency for medication follow-up, do not follow through.

He appears to derive satisfaction from his somewhat maverick role as the legitimator of a "nontraditional" agency.

> It seems to me [he told us] that I'm the supporting medical function within an organization that is largely in the nonmedical model. I certainly don't object to that, since for about thirty years I've been progressively more discouraged by what we've been able to do in traditional ways for mental illness, and I'm all for anything new that might improve our record.

The residents

The characteristics of the residents are fully as different from one program to another as are the purposes of those programs. Those living in the original halfway houses, the Quarters for Men and the Quarters for Women, have much in common with the residents of other "typical" halfway houses for the mentally ill, except that they appear to be somewhat more middle class and to have a higher educational level than the general run of state hospital patients. The supervisor for the Quarters thinks this may simply indicate that the background of the residents is representative of the community: Santa Clara is a relatively "new" county in that it has experienced very rapid growth in the past twenty years, and many of the people who have relocated there have been well-educated middle- and upper-middle-class people who were attracted by the employment opportunities in a variety of kinds of new scientific and technical enterprises. There may also be some tendency at Agnews State Hospital, from which most of the Quarters residents come, to refer such people. In any case there did not seem to be any conscious effort on the part of the staff to favor such people. Over a five-year period (1963-68) the average education of residents rose from 12 years to 12.6 years.

Over that time the residents have been quite consistent in several other characteristics. The average number of prior hospitalizations has stayed between two and three. The average age has been in the lower 30's. However, the accumulated time in hospitals has varied randomly, from a high of 41 months for the 1963-64 residents to a low of 19 months for the 1965-66 residents, and up again to 29 months for the 1967-68 residents.

By diagnosis, the substantial majority have been schizophrenics—84 percent of the men, 80 percent of the women. The others have been scattered over a number of other categories, each accounting for only one or two residents.

In a number of other halfway houses, we found that many of the residents, because they had never acquired the basic skills of social interaction or the competences of day-to-day living, required *socialization* or *habilitation* rather than *resocialization* or *rehabilitation*. The supervisor told us that the Quarters residents were a mixture: some appeared to be people who had been adequate and then became impaired in their social and "life management" skills precisely as a result of the illness; others were in the "never socialized" category,

> people who don't know how to use a deodorant, use make-up, dress appropriately. I'm thinking particularly of a girl we now have in the

Quarters who has been so sheltered that she can do hardly anything independently. She's awfully scared. We have to teach her how to do her hair, how to take a bus from one place to another and get back without being scared.

The residents of the Community Care Home are still better educated and are more solidly middle class. At the time of our visit, all of these residents had completed high school, many had finished college, and two had graduate degrees. Substantially all are acutely ill psychotics and neurotics, and both the supervisor and Mr. Goveia believed that every one of them would have required full-time hospitalization were it not for the availability of this special facility. The program does not take the high-risk suicidal patient nor the extremely agitated and disturbed psychotic but otherwise appears to accept any seriously mentally ill person thought to require 24-hour care.

During the year ended June 1969, the Community Care Home residents were people who had undergone an average of three prior hospitalizations, but for a combined total stay of less than a year (thus, a more acutely ill population than that of the Quarters). They are younger, with an average age of 25 (but a range of 16 to 45). By diagnosis, 55 percent are schizophrenic, 15 percent are personality disorders, and the rest are scattered.

Despite its rather daring notion of providing an essentially nonmedical setting as an alternative placement for people already judged to need hospitalization, the Community Care Home has had no trouble in maintaining an adequate number of referrals, and in fact has maintained a waiting list much of the time. This has resulted, curiously, in the hospitalization of the very applicants that this program was meant to keep out of the hospital; that is, almost half of those who are admitted to the house have had to spend a short time in an inpatient unit simply to await an opening at the Community Care Home.

The residents are perhaps as socially impaired as those of the Quarters, but for a different reason. The supervisor of the Community Care Home estimated that fully ninety percent of the residents are people who have limited success in and need help with their interpersonal relationships and their day-to-day living competences, but most of them, she believes, are people who at one point had these capabilities and are now handicapped precisely as the result of the acute emotional illness.

When asked why the more traditional mental health resources of the area would be willing to refer patients to this unconventional setting, Mr. Goveia said he believes it is because "we have earned a reputation of doing an effective job, but also because the people who refer residents to us value an attempt to provide an alternative to hospitalization."

Residents of the adolescent program are between sixteen and twenty. About seventy percent are referred by the courts or probation office, about twenty percent from psychiatric facilities, principally Agnews State Hospital, the rest from a variety of sources. About ninety percent have come from a facility where they were kept on a locked unit; but all are considered by RMHS to be "voluntary," irrespective of the legal basis on which they came, and all of them are free to leave at any time. RMHS requires each resident to express his desire to come, although in reality a number of them are confronted merely with a choice between this and other institutional placements. Some of them, if they should elect to leave this facility "against advice," would be faced with transfer to some other supervised setting.

Most of these young men are not psychotic by diagnosis. Said the supervisor:

> Most are the predictable products of their own past environments. Most have histories of poor parenting, deprived life circumstances, inadequate peer relationships. Most of them long ago began handling their problems by acting out and by running from responsibility and reality. Most have poor judgment, are impulsive, don't plan ahead. They decided long ago that all they're going to get is what they can try to get immediately, and they've quit looking for anything more long-range. The average age of these boys when their homes broke up was three, and this is often their fifth, sixth, or seventh institutional placement.

Very few have not used illegal drugs—perhaps twenty percent—and in fact those who have not appear to be the most seriously disordered; that is, they have been too estranged from their environment to experiment with drugs in a youth culture where drug experimentation is almost normative. About twenty percent of the boys in the program have a long-standing history of serious, heavy drug use. At the time of our visit the program was completing the intake process for a 17-year-old who had shot 32 spoons of methedrine per day for more than a year.

The residents of the Residence-Workshop are chronically ill men who have experienced multiple long hospitalizations, in frequent cases for more than fifteen years, with an average of five hospitalizations per man. They are people functioning at so low a level that they cannot qualify for other rehabilitation programs and in a number of cases have already failed in such programs as the Goodwill Industries workshop. Said the supervisor for this facility:

> Because of their chronicity, they are not "in with the stream of life." For whatever reason apart from their hospitalizations, the social growth pursuits have been denied them. Most have never married, never held responsible and fulfilling jobs, nor experienced the give-and-take of warm, human relationships. For them the struggle has been to maintain control, stay in one piece, and live with the disappointment of "not measuring up," knowing the burden they are to themselves, their loved ones, and society.

The program

All of the facilities of RMHS seem to operate under what is called a "life management" approach, in which all of the activities of each household are seen as the content of therapy—eating, grooming, cleaning the house, helping the residence manager prepare meals, hunting for jobs, and formulating plans to move into housing in the community. This regimen takes place formally in group sessions and informally in frequent spontaneous individual discussions between residents and supervisors and houseparents.

Few of the residents in any of the houses are involved in individual psychotherapy either with RMHS staff members or on the outside, and there is no evidence that there is any great interest in insight-oriented verbal psychotherapies. Rather, the therapeutic world consists of the practical realities of living and working in Santa Clara County. The program as we perceived it was infused with an aura of honesty, dignity, concern of one person for another, and a sense of freedom and reality.

The term *mental illness* is seldom used and seems, indeed, to be considered irrelevant. Instead there is a therapeutic community approach in which the actual community is used as backdrop. Anything that would add artificiality to life is undesirable; thus, assistance in learning to cope with life comes from sensitive peers and staff who, partly through serving as role models, can teach behaviors that allow for maximum autonomy in the community. Things which are "unreal," such as probing into the psyche or restricting physical movement, are antithetical to the program.

Mr. Goveia characterized the program in this way:

> We're working with people, helping them to learn how to manage their lives in the community—vocationally, financially, socially, and emotionally. We certainly don't *cure* anyone, and many of our most suc-

cessful outcomes have been clients in whom the symptomatology remained perfectly apparent, yet they managed themselves better. . . .

We may say to a client, We're not sure what sick behavior is or what sickness is, or whether you have a disease; but in terms of how society will see you, your behavior is sick, and if you keep it up, someone is going to decide that you have to be locked up. Our message is that society can stand certain kinds of behavior in certain contexts, and if you behave outside these boundaries you're in trouble.

He described the case of a resident who, despite his persisting symptomatology, was able to learn an acceptable social role.

We had a man who was talking to God, all over the neighborhood and at work. We said, Look, if you do this at work people will think you're crazy, so you'd better talk to God just here in the house. So he confined his conversations to the house. Then we said, Your conversations with God are really bugging these other men who live here, so why don't you hallucinate in the back yard? In this way, we managed to isolate his hallucinations. He continued to work, and eventually he moved to his own apartment.

RMHS does not impose a time limit at any of the facilities. However, it strives for a typical stay of about three months, and rarely does a resident remain more than six months.

Some of the houses have a house council, with the functions varying among them; in general each council is responsible for establishing and evaluating certain of the house policies, coping with problems, and making recommendations to improve the program.

The Quarters. The Quarters for Men is located next door to the offices of RMHS in a one-story, five-bedroom, two-and-a-half-bath house which has a living room, a dining room, a laundry room, and a basement. There are one single and three double bedrooms for residents, plus another bedroom for the residence manager. The house is pleasant, clean, and modest. It is located near bus lines and shopping.

The Quarters for Women is located about two miles away in a two-story, five-bedroom, two-and-a-half-bath house, which has a living room, a dining room, and a carport. There are one triple and three double bedrooms for residents, plus a single bedroom for the residence manager. Located in an established middle-class residential area, it is near public transportation and shopping.

During the day some of the Quarters residents attend the day hospital at the Central Center of the Santa Clara County Community Mental Health Services. Some attend school, others are looking for work, a few have jobs, but most are engaged in work training or evaluation through the State Department of Vocational Rehabilitation. At the house there are evening group therapy sessions run once a week by the supervisor, a weekly evaluation conference between residence manager and supervisor, including the resident when indicated, a weekly social evening, occasional community sports and entertainment events, and special dinners on some holidays.

The typical entry route is via a telephone call from the patient's social worker to the supervisor of the Quarters, at which time preliminary information is recorded and a "prestaffing" interview scheduled. Such material as psychological workups and welfare referral forms are requested. In some cases the prestaffing takes place when the prospective resident is brought to the house for a visit. Usually, however, it occurs at the hospital which has referred the patient. A week later, a "psychiatric staffing" takes place, involving the candidate, the supervisor, the psychiatrist, and any other suitable parties. If the decision is favorable, the newly accepted resident usually moves in within two or three days. Thus, typically, the complete intake process involves about ten days.

The Community Care Home. The Community Care Home is located in a large two-story house about one mile from downtown San Jose, in a middle-class residential area. It has accommodations for six men and six women residents, plus a room for the residence manager and her husband. There are two bathrooms, a laundry room, a living room, a dining room, a private counseling office for the supervisor, and a big back yard. Comfortably and conventionally furnished, the residence presents a homelike appearance.

An occasional Community Care Home resident spends his days at the day hospital. Within the house there is a group meeting each morning at which each resident reports what he is planning to do for the day. Each afternoon there is a group therapy session. Once a week there is an evening meeting involving the residents, the residence manager, and former residents. On another evening there is an educational program with various outside speakers.

The residents at the Community Care Home are expected to keep their own rooms clean and in order. The residence manager, however, does personal laundry for all of the residents.

The degree of structure deliberately built into the program is illustrated by the "guidebook" furnished to each new resident. In eighteen pages it covers in a firm but warm and friendly tone virtually every aspect of living in the house.

Referrals of prospective residents are channeled to the supervisor, who interviews the applicant, describing the program to him, evaluating his clinical status, and assessing his motivation. If the client is interested and if the supervisor believes the placement is appropriate, a psychiatric staffing is set up for a few days later.

Adolescent Residential Center (ARC). The adolescent facility is located about a half mile from RMHS administrative offices in two adjacent houses in a middle-class residential section. The larger house is the point of entry. It has three bedrooms that will house a maximum of eight residents, plus two bedrooms for live-in staff—a residence manager and one student whose job title is "role model." The smaller house next door is known as "Senior ARC"; it houses a maximum of five residents and a student role model.

During the day all of the boys attend public education and vocational programs in the vicinity. At the house there are four group therapy sessions scheduled each week, two led by the client counselor, the other two led by the residents themselves. Because these residents seem to need a great deal of feedback on a regular basis, there is a weekly "feedback session," at which each is told how the staff views his performance during the previous week. The supervisor leads a monthly two-and-a-half-hour "feedback marathon" group session including all staff and residents, discussing each resident's progress during the prior month. During the academic year there are programmed activities—recreation, arts, and crafts—from 3:30 to 5:00 each weekday afternoon. There is a particularly full recreational schedule on the weekends, with frequent outings. The live-in students provide tutoring services in some cases. During the summer the ARC program becomes a full-time day and evening educational, recreational, vocational, therapeutic activity center.

A formal "scale of functioning" has been developed, setting forth what is anticipated of each resident and providing for a numerical rating. Those who function at a level of 95 percent or better for three weeks in a row are entitled to transfer to "Senior ARC," where the privileges consist essentially of being given greater responsibility, more latitude for leaving the house to engage in outside activities, and "more emphasis on functioning through an internalized value system."

Any young man is eligible for ARC *a*) if he needs to be removed from a pathological living environment or from an environment not sufficiently structured, supervised, and supportive to meet his needs, or *b*) if he can profit "from therapeutic peer-group living and accompanying treatment and rehabilitation services." Referrals are directed to the supervisor or the counselor, who explains the program and its eligibility criteria. Thereafter, for an evidently eligible client, an appointment is made at the residence. If a referral wants to come to ARC following a visit, an intake staffing, led by the psychiatrist, is scheduled, with the applicant and the ARC supervisor both present, and at this time a decision about acceptance is made. Usually this process requires less than a week.

The Residence-Workshop. The Residence is located in a section of San Jose about two miles from the downtown area. It is a three-story, eleven-bedroom, four-bathroom home, with a dining room, a living room, and a work area in the garage. There are four double rooms and five single rooms for residents, plus two rooms for residence managers. Buses to downtown San Jose and to the Workshop are near and run frequently. A shopping section is close by.

The Workshop is located about a mile and a half from the Residence. It occupies the ground floor of a building that formerly housed a newspaper office. With almost 2000 square feet of space, it can serve comfortably as a work center for twenty or more men. There is a lunchroom which is also used for coffee and rest breaks.

The basic direction of the program is one of high structure and low to moderate expectation, with the initial goal of enabling the men to produce even at a noncompetitive level. The men are started out on quite simple jobs, and, as seems suitable, are graduated to more complex ones. Typically the residents are scheduled to work about thirty hours a week. In addition to their activities in the Workshop, there is a weekly group therapy session conducted by the supervisor, plus a weekly social evening with discussions, films, games, and crafts, plus a weekly or biweekly community activity such as attending a movie or athletic event.

The eligibility, as we have described, is limited to men functioning at a level unacceptable to other workshops. The intake procedure, with an initial interview with the supervisor followed by a "prestaffing" and a "staffing interview," is essentially the same as for the other components of RMHS.

Medication and medical service

RMHS prefers, and usually requires, that incoming residents have had a prior physical examination, largely because its own facilities for giving physical examinations are limited.

The considerable majority of the residents, except those at the adolescent facility, take psychoactive medications. From the time they come into one of the residences, each is seen by Dr. Litteral, initially each week or two weeks, then, assuming improvement takes place, every three or four weeks. He described his interviews with patients as a combined checkup on psychiatric and physical status. Those who cannot afford to pay for their own medications are given prescriptions written on special blanks that signify payment will be made by the welfare department or Medi-Cal, and these can be filled at any drugstore.

The residents can be said to be on "semi-self-medication," in that the residence manager gives each one a week's supply of medication at a time. As we have said, many of the residents who move on to other living arrangements continue to be seen by Dr. Litteral for medication supervision.

At the adolescent facility, residents who come with a psychotic diagnosis are prescribed major tranquilizers. Some of the others are prescribed antianxiety medications, either minor tranquilizers or small dosages of major tranquilizers, and hypnotics.

Outcome

For the year ended June 1969, 23 percent of the admissions to the Community Care Home were rehospitalized. This seems an impressive record for a facility whose express purpose is to serve as an alternative to hospitalization for people who have already been evaluated as requiring 24-hour care.

The Quarters for Men and the Quarters for Women can be considered a population less vulnerable to rehospitalization, since for these facilities candidates are screened in terms of anticipated rehabilitation potential. Of those admitted during the year ending mid-1968 (the latest for which complete figures were available), fifteen percent of the men and thirty percent of the women were rehospitalized either directly from these halfway houses or at some time following their move to some other abode in the community. Considering that the substantial majority are people with a lengthy history of hospitalization, with a diagnosis of schizophrenia, the results seem highly favorable.

Since the adolescent facility had been operating only a little over a year at the time of our visit, there was not sufficient experience to anticipate what its future results might be. But during the year ended June 30, 1970, 52 percent were successful outcomes using the criteria of placement in a suitable educational or training program, a satisfactory return to parents, some independent living arrangement in the community, or enlistment in one of the armed services. (This latter course is not available to those with any significant history of drug use but has not been a problem for those with a history of emotional illness who are able to pass the qualifying examination.) Placement in foster homes has been generally unavailable "since foster homes don't accept the kind of boys we're working with here."

Forty-eight percent were unsuccessful in that they had to be returned either to the juvenile court authorities or to some other facility that had jurisdiction over them.

The Residence-Workshop had been in existence less than half a year at the time of our visit—much too short a time to draw even tentative conclusions about the likely outcome of its services. Even so, we were heartened to learn that among the initial fifteen very low-functioning men, judged too limited to qualify for other workshops, only three had had to return to hospital.

Agency and community relationships

Perhaps the most important relationship of RMHS is with the county mental health program, which is its principal source of funds. It was one of the first agencies that the county contracted with to provide specialized services, and its support from the county program has grown over the years. There were said to have been some occasional concerns at the state level about the unorthodox nature of some RMHS programs; that is, they are not inpatient services in the customary sense, nor are they delimited to those things usually thought of as rehabilitation. RMHS has urged that it be considered "a different kind" of inpatient service, one which is, in fact, maintaining some seriously sick people outside the hospital, yet without the staffing requirements imposed on traditional inpatient services.

The liaison agreement with the Central Center of the Santa Clara County Community Mental Health Services network appears to be quite harmonious. This center has limited inpatient capacity and seems to be grateful that RMHS can handle some of the people from its catchment area who might otherwise have to be sent to the state hospital. Dr. Dasil Smith, chief of the county's program, told us that he anticipates a good level of continued support for RMHS.

There have been sporadic, consistently constructive, relationships with the Santa Clara County Association for Mental Health, which has helped out in times of stress and trouble, as when it made a financial contribution during the lean year following the expiration of the demonstration grant in 1959. In 1969 it contributed $2000 to assist in establishing the Residence-Workshop program. It acted as advocate for RMHS before local government officials in the face of opposition from the neighbors about opening the new adolescent facility.

Financing

During the 1970-71 fiscal year, RMHS is operating on a budget of just under $280,000, with expenses for the various facilities anticipated as follows: Quarters for Men and Quarters for Women, $39,000 each; Community Care Home, $47,000; Adolescent Residential Center, $76,-000; Residence-Workshop, $78,000.

The sources of funds are: the county's community mental health program (Short-Doyle), 46 percent; fees, 30 percent; United Fund, 13 percent; grants and other contributions, 11 percent.

The major expenses are salaries, accounting for 65 percent of expenditures. Next come rentals and food. No one of the numerous other expenses accounts for more than a small percentage of the budget.

The cost of maintaining a resident for one day varies from a low of $15.08 in the Community Care Home to a high of $20.90 in the adolescent program. These figures incorporate the overhead expenses of the administrative offices, and it should be remembered that, although not separately budgeted, included in the activities is a considerable amount of service to former residents. The costs are somewhat higher than for most other halfway houses that we know of. One perspective in which they may be viewed is as a percentage of the cost of more traditional forms of treatment. Per diem expenditures at Agnews State Hospital run to about $28 for adults and $39 for adolescents, and the cost of a day's care in the inpatient service of the community mental health center is close to $75, so that, in terms of the particular economics of the area, the RMHS programs are still far cheaper than the alternatives.

VIII. Magnificat Houses
Houston

IN TWO LARGE HOUSES, this private program can provide residence for as many as 42 people. It will accept virtually any person who needs "shelter, food, clothing, and love," with scarcely any formal eligibility requirements or criteria. Although there was no original intent of specializing in residents with a history of mental illness, as it has developed the majority of the problem-laden people who come to live there do in fact have a history of serious emotional disturbance. Operating with the help of donations from a variety of sources, this program manages to provide a very high quality of service to its residents at the remarkable cash outlay of less than a dollar per person per day.

Origins

Magnificat Houses I and II are the brainchild of an extraordinary woman who always has been and continues to be the vital, driving force behind their development and operation. Rose Mary Badami, a native of Houston, after earning a bachelor's degree in sociology, accepted a job as a social worker at the Convent of the Good Shepherd, an institution for delinquent girls, where she was deeply troubled by their circumstances.

> Many didn't have parents or a decent place to live, had never known the odor of home cooking or a mother to greet them at the door. They stayed with us about a year, then went back to the same old environment, often to homes where they weren't wanted. So I thought, What they need is someone who will accept them as they are, stick with them, let them know that no matter what they do they have a home and someone who is going to love them.

Miss Badami stayed with the Good Shepherd for several years, keeping in contact with many of the girls who went on to the state reformatory. Then in 1964 she determined to start a home for girls and women leaving state reformatories and penal institutions. With the assistance of

Father Denis Mary McAuliffe and later Monsignor James J. Madden, and operating through the Legion of Mary, volunteers were recruited to start a special group to plan for the home. One local woman offered the use of a small house rent free for up to a year, a recent widow agreed to serve as full-time housemother without salary, and two working girls volunteered to contribute toward the utilities and food bills. Representatives of the group went to the local prison where the warden agreed to use the hostel in its prerelease program. The new home filled up quickly and ran without incident until, about eight months later, it accepted a young Negro girl. The neighbors rose up in protest. The woman who owned the house requested they not take any more Negro girls because she had known the neighbors for a long time and didn't want to offend them. And so, Miss Badami said:

> We decided then and there to stick by our principles. We decided that if it was God's will, which surely it must be, we would find the means to get established in another house.

Several people who became sympathetic to the plight in which the hostel found itself each offered some financial support, and enough funds were amassed to meet most of the cost of purchasing a house. Thereafter, the program flourished, albeit informally—there was no board of directors, merely interested individuals in those days—and on a very modest budget that depended largely on contributions. This hostel was eventually incorporated and became a recognized charitable organization, as it continues to the present time, providing residence for eleven young women.

HAVING ACCOMPLISHED THIS SUCCESSFUL OUTCOME, Miss Badami decided to move on to other efforts. Her involvement was entirely private and personal; because there were no funds to pay her a salary, and because she must provide for her aged parents, she has worked, as a teacher of retarded children, throughout the years that she has developed the program. In 1968, when she received a raise in pay that yielded her an additional $52 per month after taxes, she decided to use this money toward establishing a home for adult women, including those with children.

At about this time, she received a call from the woman who had made the original house available to her rent free; the neighborhood had become integrated, the house was vacant, and it was once more available for a time at no cost. Thus, with the free rent and the $52 a month from her own salary, Miss Badami established Magnificat House I. An older alcoholic woman that she had known from the hostel came in as house-mother. A retired seaman, his "shell-shocked" friend, and several other volunteers came, painted and repaired the house without charge. Miss Badami started a monthly newsletter for interested persons and groups to report progress at Magnificat House and to solicit contributions.

Knowing that she could stay in the rent-free premises only a few months, she sought a house to buy and the money to buy it with. Her retired seaman friend came to her astonished aid, pledging six thousand dollars toward the cost. Thus, in November 1968 the original Magnificat House moved to its present quarters. Borrowing the name of the St. Vincent de Paul Society in order to avoid tax liability, Magnificat House solicited furniture and contributions both of money and time. Many needed repairs and painting were done by volunteers. Absolutely nothing in the attractive, comfortably furnished house had to be bought or paid for except a clothes dryer.

Within a few months, Miss Badami had become greatly concerned about the need for a house for men. A particularly large vacant house several miles away came to her attention. Owned by a foundation, it was being vandalized. The owners were receptive to her proposal that another residence be established there, rent free, for as long as the foundation owned the house. Thus Magnificat House II came into existence in September 1969. As of the time of our visit in early 1970, the foundation had no plans to put the house on the market.

Physical facilities

Magnificat House I, exclusively for women, is a two-story frame house on a corner lot in a lower-middle-class neighborhood, conveniently located to public transportation and shopping. The house is attractive and well maintained. It is on a large, nicely landscaped lot.

The first floor has a living room and dining room of good size, a reasonably modern kitchen, a pantry, a bathroom, and a bedroom for the two housemothers. Upstairs are four bedrooms accommodating twelve women, and a bathroom. The appearance throughout is light and cheerful, comfortable and homelike.

There is a large garage with a four-room apartment upstairs that houses six additional residents.

Magnificat House II, primarily for men, is located on a principal avenue in a mixed commercial-residential area. On a one-and-a-half-acre lot, it is relatively isolated. The main house is exceptionally large. The ground floor consists of two living rooms, one used as a meeting room, the other as a lounge, a dining room, a kitchen, an office, and two bedrooms and bathrooms. Upstairs are six large bedrooms and four bathrooms. There are accommodations for twenty men.

A cottage in back of the house contains a living room, a kitchen, two bedrooms, and a bathroom; it is used for four single women.

The program is pleased to have a facility whose layout makes it possible to accommodate both men and women. "Many of our residents have never experienced a normal relationship with a member of the opposite sex," said Miss Badami. "Since we hope that they will be moving on to a regular social life in the community, we feel it is best for them to learn or relearn social relationships in a controlled situation such as Magnificat House II provides."

The staff

Among the more remarkable aspects of this program are *a*) it has no paid staff and *b*) most of the people who carry out the customary staff functions are former state hospital patients.

Miss Badami, as founder, president of the board, and the motive force for the houses, is by all odds the most consequential staff member. But because of her full-time employment elsewhere, she is customarily available only after regular working hours and on weekends. She attends weekly house meetings at each of the houses, and comes by on any evening when a serious problem arises or a particular resident seems to need special attention. But she does not feel it necessary to visit each house every evening or to spend all her weekend hours there. Most evenings she does have a telephone conversation with one of the staff members from each house.

The "co-housemothers" at the women's house and the housemother at the men's house are all women who were patients at the state hospital serving the Houston area. All were hospitalized for several years before Miss Badami approached them about accepting the posts at the halfway houses. They receive free room and board and $50 per month each to cover personal incidental expenses. In our interviews, each of these women expressed her gratitude for having found a place outside the hospital where she could do useful work and have a life of her own. All three impressed us as highly competent, self-assured, warm, empathic women who were altogether appropriate for the demands of their work. While each had to accept a good deal of personal responsibility and was expected to operate with quite a bit of autonomy, it was nonetheless evident that they regarded Miss Badami as the person they turned to without hesitation when problems arose. It was also evident that they regarded her with a great deal of respect, love, and gratitude. From their histories, each had evidently been seriously impaired by mental illness, but quite possibly would never have needed to undergo hospitalization in a state hospital had there been available a suitable community placement such as Magnificat House.

For the most part, the house staff have never been given formalized responsibilities. "Each one does the things she feels comfortable with," Miss Badami said. "One loves to cook and keep house, the other to do contact work with agencies, job placement, handling correspondence, and so on. It has worked out very well. It would be presumptuous of me to tell them how to run their own house."

The duties at Magnificat House II are roughly divided into "interior" and "exterior." The housemother is responsible for overseeing the cooking, cleaning, and various other aspects of running the house. The male staff member, also a former state hospital patient, is in charge of the grounds, including a very large rose garden, and maintaining the exterior of the house. (The men residents also take care of the grounds at the women's house.)

During the few months of its existence prior to our visit, Magnificat House II had recruited, and dismissed, two pairs of young houseparents who did not have any history of mental illness. On the supposition that because the house intended to cater to men and to women it would be desirable to have a couple, Miss Badami advertised in a national specialty publication, offering only room and board and the stipend of $50 per month each. The first couple were "hippie" in attitude and behavior and entirely neglected to clean either the house or themselves. The second couple, "more appreciative of social norms," turned out to be too young—they were only 24 and 22 years old—to exercise the authority and provide the support that was needed from them.

The housemother at the men's house made what seemed a logical case for deliberately staffing a halfway house with people who have been hospitalized for mental illness.

> It is really a good thing that the staff members have been in the state hospital. From watching the attendants and the doctors we learned a lot that helps us to help the residents. As soon as they realize our own background, they feel more at home and assured that they'll be treated well and will be understood. I'm glad that I've been there so that I can help these people.

As far as we know, the practice of putting former mental patients in charge of programs for other former mental patients is relatively untried.

(In recent years some mental health facilities, notably state hospitals, have started to employ a few people who were formerly patients, but these are often low-level jobs that are highly supervised.) If one really believes that some of the people with a history of mental illness can be rehabilitated and, with proper supports, can be productive and effective in community roles, then to select certain ones to help recovering mental patients has a great deal of appeal. We are not proposing that every person who comes out of a state hospital would be suitable to become an employee of a halfway house, but with careful selection there are undoubtedly some that would do as well as or perhaps better than many people who have not been mentally ill. In any case, the arrangement at the two Magnificat Houses was exciting and thrilling to see. Here were relationships operating to the advantage of everyone concerned. These houseparents, none of whom had families suitable to return to, had found work to do that suited their capabilities and made them feel useful; the residents benefited from the special understanding and support that the staff members seemed uniquely qualified to give them; and the houses were provided the services of suitable people that could be afforded within a very limited budget. (Miss Badami several times expressed the wish that she had enough money to pay more than $50 per month, and one of the staff members spoke of the problems of having an adequate amount of clothes with this limited income.)

We felt that it was a tribute to Miss Badami that she was able to accept people entirely for the jobs they can do and for their personal qualities rather than to categorize them by any diagnostic label or stigmatize them for having been in a mental hospital. Said Dr. Elpers, "If more people could be this accepting, many of our psychiatric rehabilitation efforts would be unnecessary."

We discussed this matter of using untrained former patients both with the rehabilitation counselor who follows clients placed at the houses by the Division of Vocational Rehabilitation and with the psychiatrist at the community mental health center serving the catchment area in which the women's house is located (the center refers some of the residents and provides psychiatric service to some of the others). Neither felt any concern. The rehabilitation counselor said that "the informal and homelike atmosphere that results, it seems to me, is very helpful to the residents, and I don't think that having trained staff members would make us feel any better about having our clients live here." The psychiatrist said that "there may be some advantages to there being no live-in professional staff. I think it works out to be less formal, so that the patient feels more at home."

The staff members are assisted by particular residents designated as "resident helpers." Having proven themselves reliable, they are authorized to be left in charge of the houses when the staff members must be away. There are two at the women's house and five at the men's house.

A great deal of important help is provided by the treasurer of the board, Mrs. Florence O'Haren, a long-time friend of Miss Badami who is also a licensed dietitian. Entirely as a volunteer, she plans the menus, helps the staff in buying, does the bookkeeping, and handles the finances of both houses. These activities consume about three hours a day. On the evenings that Miss Badami is not available for backup call from the houses, Mrs. O'Haren substitutes for her.

Adult volunteers have provided a great variety of services, ranging from free professional time to plumbing repairs. Much of this has been on an *ad hoc* basis. One notably regular volunteer is an older man who learned of the house from a newspaper story. A religious counselor at the YMCA, he was led by the description of the program to pay a visit. He immediately volunteered his time. He spends about one and a half days a week substituting for house staff on their days off.

A number of young volunteers have been involved through the Catholic Youth Organization and other membership groups. One group helped to paint the first house. Another fixed Thanksgiving and Christmas baskets. Another has organized drives to obtain donations of furniture, food, and household supplies. Several have invited staff members to come and speak to them, and several have visited the houses.

The residents

Both in philosophy and in day-to-day operation, the policy of Magnificat Houses is to admit anyone in need. Any person who needs refuge will be taken on an emergency basis, and this has extended to the point of accepting a family of five, at midnight, to sleep on cots and couches. (Miss Badami expressed some bewilderment that any helping agency would ever refuse to take in any person in need.)

"Formal" admission requires a determination that the individual will be able to get along in the group-living arrangement that characterizes the houses. Scarcely ever is anyone excluded on the grounds that he would not fit in. The only preadmission information required is a one-page form. One of the housemothers, asked whether background information from a hospital would be helpful, replied that "what is more helpful is for the residents to know that we don't question their background too much and that they start here with a clean slate."

Because the houses are operated to help any category of person in need, they request no medical, social, or psychological information from referring institutions, are not interested in the diagnoses of the people referred, and pay no attention to failures, inappropriate behavior, or problems of the past. As it turns out, many of the residents have a history of mental illness. At the time of our visit, twelve of the sixteen residents at the women's house had been hospitalized at some time in the past for mental illness, and the majority of these had come to the house directly from a treatment facility. There are also some with alcoholism problems (particularly among the men), occasional ex-convicts, and mental retardates.

A psychiatrist from the Texas Research Institute of Mental Sciences told us that he reserves referrals to people who have no money to pay, since placements such as Magnificat House are quite scarce. He feels that the houses do well with "burned out" schizophrenics, psychotics in remission, borderline psychotics, and severe neurotics. He especially singles out for referral those who "require tolerance of their deviant behavior."

Magnificat House does not worry about which groups it does poorly with, since the stated purpose is to take everyone, including those who from a statistical standpoint do not do well. However, there have been bad experiences with four teen-age drug abusers, three of whom were residents simultaneously; the staff was unable to handle the disruptions and discipline problems that they caused, and eventually all four were sent back to the hospital. Otherwise, only two men had been expelled in the six months that Magnificat House II had been operating, and no one, in two and a half years, had ever been expelled from the women's house. (However, two women have been found other living arrangements "because they chose to dominate and control instead of becoming a part of the group.")

While the program receives referrals from numerous sources, in practice some specialization emerges. Specifically, in terms of referral sources, Magnificat House sees itself as primarily serving the following groups:

From the state hospital, patients "whom it becomes possible to discharge because we will take responsibility for them"

From the local municipal general hospital, discharged patients who have no place to go

From the Texas Research Institute of Mental Sciences, clients still receiving supervised treatment

From the Texas Youth Council, juveniles seventeen years old and over who have been paroled from reformatories and who will not be returning to school

From the welfare department, temporarily unemployable clients

From the Division of Vocational Rehabilitation, persons enrolled in DVR-sponsored training programs

From the Travelers Aid Society, temporary placements from out of town.

A number of referrals also come from Ripley House, an agency that is incorporated into the program of the Mid-Houston Community Mental Health Center; these are day hospital patients who need housing.

The program

If a resident at Magnificat House is involved with some treating, training, or other service agency, the house sees that agency as having primary responsibility for formulating a plan for the resident; the goal of the house is thus to encourage that plan rather than to formulate one of its own. A number of residents are clients of the Division of Vocational Rehabilitation, under whose sponsorship they are financed in various kinds of training programs.

For those who do not have a daytime program, Magnificat House has scheduled activities. In the morning each person is expected to clean his own room and to help with household chores and the outside work. In the afternoon the women engage on various days in sewing, cooking, grooming, and a decorating class. The men spend their afternoons gardening, doing carpentry, and attending volunteer-led classes in language skills, health and nutrition, and arts and crafts.

One evening a week is devoted to a house meeting where staff and residents meet for assignment of house duties and to discuss any problems of running the house. A volunteer professional counselor and Miss Badami attend these meetings. On another evening a social worker and job counselor are on hand to counsel any resident who has the need. On Wednesday evening there is a group therapy session conducted by a psychologist. On Friday evening the residents frequently go in a group to a nearby motion picture theater which furnishes free admission. On Sunday transportation is provided to the Catholic church located at some distance, while Protestants walk to the Presbyterian church located five blocks away. Twice a month the two houses get together for a buffet dinner and a social.

Most important to the Magnificat House philosophy is that no time limit is set. To do so would be altogether antithetical to the persuasion that *a*) what the individual needs most is an awareness that he is welcome, *b*) he should experience Magnificat House as his home, and *c*) he will be welcome as long as he needs to stay. At the same time, the average stay is not long compared with other halfway houses, and in fact the modal stay falls between one week and one month. The staff would not feel comfortable if the houses should simply fill up with people who were all terminal, because this "would not be realizing our purpose." Said Mrs. O'Haren:

> We don't let people pull the wool over our eyes. We don't let them say, Well, I won't try to get a job because I know I can't find one. We know when it is time to say, All right, you're more stable now, enough so to think about leaving the nest.

Although there is no formal provision for recruiting jobs and placing the residents in them, the informal approach has by and large worked well. In some cases Miss Badami has scouted out jobs for residents. More often, the resident has found his own, through friends or through classified advertisements. However, if the program had more money one of the things it would add would be a vocational placement specialist.

Medication and medical service

Every person who becomes a formal resident—that is, stays beyond a day or two of emergency shelter—must have a blood test and a chest X ray; the program has arranged to have these done free at a local clinic.

All of the residents who have been mental illness patients are under the supervision of some local treating agency, in most cases the Ripley House component of the Mid-Houston Community Mental Health Center or the Texas Research Institute of Mental Sciences. Most are on psychoactive medication, which in most cases is obtained from these same facilities. There has rarely been a problem about obtaining the drugs prescribed for the residents, and when one cannot qualify to receive the medicine without cost and has no money, the house pays for it.

Magnificat House attaches great importance to medication. In each house the housemothers keep the medication in locked cabinets, then distribute it in medicine cups at mealtime. This is done both to remind the residents to take it, and to avoid any case of one person taking another's medication.

Outcome

Magnificat House has not carried out any formal study of what happens to its residents after they leave. Because of the philosophy it operates under, it would seem to gain nothing from such a study other than to satisfy the curiosity of the staff, the board, and the contributors. At the same time, quite a lot is known informally about what happens to the people who have lived there. For one thing, very few return to psychiatric facilities—only about eleven in the year prior to our visit, and most of these were women who, having already been diagnosed as requiring hospitalization, were being provided temporary shelter until the necessary arrangements could be made. Some residents return to their families. More take their own apartments, sometimes alone but typically to share with others. When a resident is trying to save money to pay the advance rent on an apartment, Magnificat House excuses him from paying room and board during the final month of residence. There is no formal procedure for planning the resident's departure and post-Magnificat House placement. The staff merely talk with the resident, trying to point out some of the realistic factors that face him, then let him make his own decisions.

A program that pays no salary to its director and only incidental expense money to its staff members, goes from door to door soliciting food, and relies on cash donations to meet its minimal expenses cannot be faulted because it has not done an outcome study. However, the evidently good results of this program are such that it would be extremely useful if some outside agency were to be given access to the records in order to do a formal study, in the interest of seeing whether the outcome is not at least as good as that of other programs that are much more selective, much more highly staffed, and operating at a per diem expense many times that of Magnificat House.

Agency and community relationships

From all that we could tell, Magnificat House enjoys extremely good relationships with the various agencies who send clients to it and from whom the house seeks services for the residents. The wish was expressed that a particular one of the treating agencies would sometimes move more rapidly to accept as clients the residents which Magnificat House refers to it. There have been problems with another treating agency about referring prospective residents to the welfare department prior to referring them to Magnificat House—the difference being that, if referred first to the house and accepted, welfare would then refuse to pay their room and board.

There have been no problems with neighbors of either house. No efforts were made to "prepare" the neighborhood and the interaction with neighbors is quite limited.

Financing

The actual cash outlay per resident as of the time of our visit early in 1970 was seventy-seven cents per day. This is of course not the real cost, since one of the houses is rent free and both rely strongly on donations of goods and services. Even so, and particularly when one considers that the accommodations are attractive and comfortable, the food well prepared and varied, this must be considered a staggering accomplishment.

The principal sources of revenue during the first nine months of 1969, when only the women's house was in operation, were as follows: individual contributions from residents, 44 percent; cash donations, 35 percent; payments from the welfare department, 17 percent; profit from special projects, three percent; payments from Travelers Aid, two percent.

Those residents who are able to pay are asked to contribute $20 per week for room and board. The majority of these are people in training programs under Division of Vocational Rehabilitation sponsorship. DVR provides $120 per month directly to the client to cover all living expenses; Magnificat House asks for $20 per week, leaving the client a reasonable amount for transportation and incidental expenses. Magnificat House would like to become approved itself as a DVR-allied halfway house, since it could then receive payments directly and at a much higher rate. Not all the residents are DVR clients, of course, and during 1969 the contributions from residents averaged only $24 per resident per month.

Much of the deficit is made up by donations, which are obtained principally through solicitations in the monthly Magnificat House newsletter. These donations in 1969 averaged about $345 per month.

Occasional residents are welfare clients—but only if they have already been approved for welfare payments before they move to Magnificat House. As we have indicated, should the house find itself obliged to accept an indigent person before he has been qualified by welfare, the department takes the position that he is already provided for and thus ineligible. Welfare in Harris County, Texas, provides $50 per month for room and board. Funds from this source amounted to a total of $167 per month during 1969.

The small amount of funds from Travelers Aid represents payment to Magnificat House for providing temporary emergency shelter to destitute people from out of town, at the rate of $3 per day for room and board.

Of the projected 1970 expenditures of just under $900 per month for both houses, the largest item, 34 percent, is food. Next come the "stipends" of $50 a month each for four staff members. Then, the expenses of operating and maintaining two older automobiles and a ten-year-old truck used for picking up donated furniture, clothing, and food. No other item accounts for as much as ten percent of the budget.

Much of the food is donated, and one of the staff members regularly goes to the farmers' market to see if there are unsold vegetables that will be given to the house (as there frequently are). We have described how the houses were furnished with contributed furniture and repaired and maintained with donated labor. Said Miss Badami:

> People are willing to give. They want to. All our furniture was donated, and you can see that the chairs don't match, but what difference does that make? I wouldn't want to have money to go out and buy all these things. I want people to give. We could furnish I don't know how many houses with what people have in their garages.

The strong religious belief of Miss Badami and the staff causes them to feel that there is no need to be ashamed or embarrassed in soliciting money and goods as they do. On occasion staff members have gone from door to door asking for contributions of canned goods.

A few months before our visit Mrs. O'Haren had arranged a food and clothing drive through a youth organization in her church. More than $300 worth of canned food was donated, and enough clothing to begin a "garage sale." One of the staff members told us:

> Three of us from the staff appeared before the congregation and told them about the nature of our work, and they realized that this was a program with a special quality and not just another mission that will give someone a meal and a night's lodging. By the end of two days the small building in back of the church was overflowing with food and clothing and furniture. It took us almost a week just to go back and forth with the pickup truck to get it all.

But this is not to say that Miss Badami and her board of directors would not like to have more money. For one thing, they would like to be able to pay Miss Badami a salary equivalent to what she earns as a schoolteacher, so that she could quit her outside employment and devote her full time to the houses and to others that she would be able to start. And they would like enough money to pay the staff members more than the present $50 a month for incidental expenses. These seem quite modest desires for a program that serves so many people with such evidently good effect and at such a remarkably low cost. One wonders if the fervor and zeal that characterize these houses would diminish if unlimited funds should suddenly become available. In any case, it seems indicative of the program that Miss Badami would not ever want that time to come; despite the desire to have enough money to extend and expand staff services, she and her associates will continue to see the process of giving as one of the most important ingredients of Magnificat House.

IX. The Lodge/Labor Saver Service, Inc.
Fort Logan Mental Health Center
Denver

FORT LOGAN MENTAL HEALTH CENTER, a modern facility which is one of Colorado's two state hospitals, came into being in 1961. With an unusually comprehensive treatment approach developed from the concept of the therapeutic community, it is, as it always has been, a completely "open" hospital with a major commitment to enable as many of its patients as possible to assume competent, autonomous roles in community living. From the outset Fort Logan has emphasized treatment at the lowest level of intensity compatible with the patient's needs, and thus has usually had at least as many patients on day status as on inpatient status, and still more on outpatient status. It has a highly trained professional staff, with a good ratio of staff to patient, and at the same time has made a major and important effort to incorporate carefully chosen "nonprofessionals" into the treatment teams, with a distinct "flattening of hierarchy." This much-visited hospital seems to have had an important influence on many other treatment facilities, particularly in terms of formulating a program focused more on the needs of patients than on the needs of staff members.

Fort Logan had not been long in business, however, before it became evident that a certain percentage of patients who would not respond to treatment and instead would remain in the hospital or would be indefinitely involved in a constant discharge and readmission process threatened to develop into so large a residual population as to take up the total capacity of the hospital.

In 1967, one of the consultants involved in the present study (Miles), who was then the chief of vocational services for Fort Logan, became acquainted with the work of Dr. George Fairweather and his associates at the Palo Alto (California) Veterans Administration Hospital, where a "lodge" had been established off the hospital grounds, for the purpose of providing supports to long-term chronic patients in the hope of enabling them to become self-supporting and to live in the community.[1] Dr. Miles went to Palo Alto to study the program, then only two years old. He returned to Fort Logan filled with enthusiasm and presented the details of the program to the Fort Logan staff, who decided to develop a lodge program in downtown Denver, ten miles away from the hospital.

Dr. Fairweather's work indicated that the ideal constituency of the group would be about equal numbers of verbal, socially active patients and withdrawn, inactive patients. With this in mind, a Fort Logan staff committee chose from 37 candidates 19 men with a long and/or frequent history of hospitalization. Among these were some with chronic alcoholism and character disorders, since men with these conditions had been found to do well in the Palo Alto program. Fifteen of these 19 chose to become part of the Lodge program.

In mid-1967, the 15 men, while continuing as 24-hour patients, were brought together during the day to spend a month working as a group at particular assigned tasks of a routine nature and renovating the facility that they were to move to in the community. After this preparation, they moved into their new living quarters. There an additional month was spent in getting organized. A janitorial service was established, the men were trained to do the tasks involved, and a staff member set about attempting to obtain work for them to do.

About 18 months later the group moved to its present quarters. Then, in February 1969, the members organized themselves into an autonomous nonprofit corporation taking the name of Labor Saver Service, Inc., with a six-man board of directors composed of business and professional leaders in the community plus one of the Lodge members.

Physical facilities

The Lodge is located in a lower-middle-class section of "intown" Denver, in an older building that was originally a small apartment house. A central entry and stairway divides the building, but all of the former apartments are now kept open so that the building is used in effect as a large house. On the first floor are a large double living room, a large dining room, and a well-equipped kitchen.

The second floor and basement contain the sleeping quarters, which can accommodate a maximum of eighteen. The former apartments are relatively barren, which may be somewhat diagnostic of the severity of

[1] This important rehabilitation effort is fully described in G. Fairweather: *Community Life for the Mentally Ill: An Alternative to Institutional Care.* Aldine Publishing Co., Chicago, 1969.

pathology of these men, for while there was a great group concern about cleanliness, there seemed to be none about the bare rooms. In the back yard is a small building with two rooms, one used to store the tools used in their work program, the other set up as a small assembly shop for a work project contracted from Fort Logan.

Despite the lack of warmth and color in the house, the men appeared to be comfortable with it. The space was more than ample. While some outside group could no doubt be recruited to improve the furnishings and decoration, such a move might very well interfere with the group process arourd which the entire program is focused.

The neighborhood is a reasonably convenient one, with shopping and public transportation nearby.

The staff

A most remarkable aspect of the Lodge program is that it requires almost no staff. When the program was initiated, two Fort Logan staff members were assigned to it. Dr. Ladd MacDonald, in a paper describing the Lodge, says:

> In what turned out to be a fortuitous choice, two staff members were hired to assist the group in its development. Neither of these had any professional training in mental health work. One, the group worker, was a graduate student in speech at Denver University and was majoring in communications methodology. The other, responsible for obtaining the initial work contracts for the group, had a business background. The group worker's responsibility was primarily one of encouraging the fifteen discrete individuals to become a unified, functional group. The fact that the group was task oriented, dealing with day-to-day problems, enabled the group worker and the contracts solicitor to help the individuals develop constructive methods of problem solving. The group worker encouraged effective interpersonal communication and assisted the group in setting up a leadership and organizational structure. Thus, we had one staff member for each of the two overlapping concerns of the group: developing the social aspects and developing the business aspects. . . . Their lay status enabled them to see many of the issues which emerged as issues per se rather than as "psychiatric issues." The practical, matter-of-fact approach which derived from this orientation was a definite asset. Fortunately, they also developed responsive and open relationships with the patients, which enhanced the development of the group. Both continually operated on the premise that the fifteen individuals would ultimately become independent and self-sufficient as a group, and that each individual could handle a maximum amount of responsibility.

After the first year, because it was felt he was no longer needed, the group worker was withdrawn from the program, which since then has functioned solely with the business manager. He is on the Fort Logan payroll as a vocational counselor. His main responsibilities are locating jobs, keeping the books, and maintaining liaison with Fort Logan. Beyond this, he acknowledged only a passive and supportive role toward the members, to whom he reflects back nearly all problems involving decision making, personal adjustment, and even clinical intervention. (In reality, it seemed to us, he frequently provides skilled nondirective counseling, in a style that offers support but avoids authoritarian direction, with the goal of helping the residents to stay aware of and assume ultimate responsibility for all of their own decisions.) It is planned that the Fort Logan Lodge will eventually follow the model of the prototype program in Palo Alto and become completely autonomous and independent of staff assistance.

Dr. Richard Stadter, chief of the community services department of Fort Logan, serves as consultant. He works principally through the group, rarely with individual members. He does, however, maintain medication supervision. Deeply interested in the program and highly motivated to work in community psychiatry, he sees a great need for additional lodge programs, including some that would serve women patients. In fact, he believes that there are very few patients who cannot be successfully treated and maintained in the community.

From time to time in the past, members of particular Fort Logan treatment teams have come to visit the Lodge to see patients they have referred there. More recently this kind of visit has been discouraged. Said Harold Berberick, acting chief of the vocational services department at Fort Logan:

> In a sense, they brought the culture of the hospital to the Lodge. Many times the patients acted sicker when hospital staff members came in and talked to them.

The residents

Candidates for the Lodge are referred by the treatment teams at Fort Logan. Prospective residents must exhibit two primary qualities: *a*) a demonstrated *inability* to function in the community without a socially supportive living arrangement and *b*) a demonstrated *inability* to work successfully in the competitive labor market. Beyond this, each candidate is required to meet the eligibility requirements for "extended evaluation" support from the Colorado Division of Rehabilitation, which is the major source of funds. Admittance to the program is then subject to a favorable vote by a majority of the current residents. Each new member is placed on probation for a period of one month.

Of 23 men who resided in the house during 1969, ten were between 21 and 30 years old; two were between 30 and 40; one was between 40 and 50; nine were between 50 and 60; and one was more than 60. Thus there is a bimodal distribution, with all but four of these 23 residents falling either between 21 and 30 or between 50 and 60. Their average length of stay in mental hospitals was a little more than five years.

Of ten men who left the house during 1969, the length of stay was as follows:

Under one week	2
One week to one month	1
One to three months	2
Four to six months	1
Six months to one year	2
Over two years	2

Of fourteen men who were residents in mid-1969, six had been diagnosed as schizophrenic, six as alcoholics, one as manic-depressive, and one as having a brain syndrome. None were currently married; seven were either divorced or separated, and seven others had never been married. One had completed college and some graduate work, seven others had finished high school, and the remaining six had completed from five to 11 years of schooling. Most had worked at unskilled and semiskilled occupations prior to hospitalization, and two had never worked at all. During their first six months of residence at the Lodge, none worked less than 19 out of the 26 weeks, and 11 of the 14 worked every week.

The program

The Lodge can be described as a "psychorehabilitative commune," designed to help its members achieve self-sufficiency in the community. The program provides a living experience in which its members live together, work together, manage money affairs and daily routines together. An occasional resident leaves the program to live autonomously in the community, but by and large the Lodge is conceived of as a terminal facility. Thus, the residents are encouraged to remain in the program indefinitely, since a basic tenet of the Lodge is that in order for the long-term psychiatric patient to adjust satisfactorily to the community a considerable amount of extended support must be available both in the work and living situations. For this group, the developers of the Lodge feel that the concept of "cure" in any traditional sense is unrealistic. For example, of thirteen patients who left the Lodge from July of 1969 to May of 1970, over half returned to the hospital and only one was able to secure employment.

The relationship between the Lodge and Fort Logan is loosely structured. Fort Logan treatment personnel refer the prospective resident to the hospital's vocational services department, which in turn refers him to the Lodge, where, if he is accepted by those already in the program, he becomes a member.

It is at this point that the quality of relationship between the Lodge and Fort Logan becomes unique. The Fort Logan staff, particularly Dr. Stadter and those in the vocational services department, remain loosely in touch with the patient, to be of help when intervention seems required. But this is not a formal or systematic kind of follow-up, nor one in which the Fort Logan staff play an authoritative role. Rather, the Lodge population themselves assume responsibility for assessing each member's progress, including his need for backup services by the hospital staff. Typically, the Lodge members themselves make the decision that intervention is called for, or, occasionally, that a member needs to return to the hospital. The hospital stands ready to accept any patient back without question—but with a forcefully put admonition. "We repeatedly emphasize to the Lodge residents," Dr. Ethel Bonn, director of Fort Logan, told us, "that we have no magic. We can provide the safeguards that are needed in order to administer larger doses of medication than would be appropriate outside a hospital, but beyond this we feel that the milieu of the Lodge itself is perhaps as beneficial and supportive as what we can provide in the hospital." Consequently, Lodge members who are readmitted to Fort Logan typically stay a very short time, often no more than a week.

This relationship conveys to the members that the Fort Logan staff will be available in time of crisis; also, it fosters a feeling of mutual concern and interdependency among the Lodge residents, of caring for each other, and of establishing their own standards for acceptable behavior. While the men will tolerate a considerable range of behavior among themselves, seriously disruptive behavior rarely occurs.

E ACH WORKING DAY BEGINS AT THE LODGE with a meeting of all residents. The men take seats in the living room, relaxed in the comfortable if somewhat run-down furnishings. The meeting is conducted by a group chairman, a resident elected by his fellow residents for an indefinite term.

The affairs of the house are reviewed. They include work assignments, new job possibilities, reports on assignments completed, and so on. On the morning that we attended this meeting, there was a discussion about a resident who had recently been hospitalized for internal bleeding; two residents agreed to visit him. Two jobs scheduled for the truck crew for that day were described. One resident who had become skillful in estimating the cost of such jobs reported on a new moving job and what would be involved. A brief discussion followed about who would drive the truck, and the chairman appointed one of the men. The meeting also included matters of housekeeping, menus, furniture acquisition, and coming events. The process seemed to work well; there was relatively little affect but nonetheless a prevailing feeling of openness and mutuality among the men, as well as a sense of common purpose and a notable lack of quibbling about responsibilities and assignments.

Labor Saver Service, as the work component of the program is known, has its own new truck and extensive equipment to carry out a variety of cleaning, hauling, and janitorial jobs. The most frequent type of work is cleaning houses repossessed by the Veterans Administration. Some months before our visit the men had had a contract for cleaning Denver's football stadium after each game, and they hoped to increase this kind of work.

There has frequently been a problem in acquiring enough work to keep the men busy. For this reason there have been several subcontracts with the Fort Logan work therapy program, to fill the gaps. For the most part, the men have not worked much more than half time.

The work assignments are made by a committee consisting of the house chairman, the business manager, and two members. Jobs are priced at the minimum wage and above. During the first two years of the Lodge, the total amount earned each week was simply divided by the number of men who had done any work at all, so that each received an equal amount. More recently, the earnings have been divided according to each member's actual hours of work.

All of the residents who are not physically ill take part in the work assignments, with the exception of two who work within the house, as the cook and the cook's assistant. These positions have been allocated because of the men's belief that apportioning the cooking, in addition to the outside work, would be too stressful for some of the residents. All of the men take turns washing dishes and cleaning the common rooms, and each man does his own laundry.

APART FROM THE WORK ASSIGNMENTS on the outside and within the house, there is little else in the way of a structured program. The men return from work, have dinner together, and then use the house much as they would an old-fashioned boardinghouse; for all practical purposes, they are on their own. There are no planned social activities, no group counseling programs. Activities take place spontaneously, with relationships forming naturally. One resident told us that the men divide about equally into those who retreat to their own rooms to be alone and those who engage in socializing or watching television within the house or going out to the movies or a nearby tavern.

The success of the Lodge is evidenced by the outcome data presented below. At this point, it seems well to quote the report of one of the consultants (Rutman) following our visit to this program.

> If traditionally oriented mental health professionals could see the Lodge in operation and could know of the results with its members, many of them would find it mind-boggling. Given the picture of chronicity and the advanced ages of many members, the program is astonishing in that it functions as a largely self-contained and self-sufficient facility, with only one full-time staff member, with a net operating cost of about $5 per man per day, and simultaneously serves as a residence, a jointly owned business operation, and a kind of therapeutic community.

We interviewed two of the men living at the Lodge. We asked one of them, a man who had been hospitalized six times over a period of years with manic-depressive psychosis:

Q. What do you like better about living here than being in the hospital?

A. Well, for one thing, I can help and support myself, and that means a whole lot. I just can't seem to make it on the outside. I still have problems, but with the group's help, I think I can make it. When I get nervous and tense on the job, the group talks to me and quiets me down.

Q. Would you like to stay here permanently?

A. Yes, I would, under the circumstances. I'll be sixty years old next month and as far as I'm concerned the outside is pretty rough.

Q. Is there anything you would like to see changed about the program?

A. We've had some improvements since I've been here. One important thing is the ability of the group to get along together and use itself almost like group therapy at Fort Logan.

Medication and medical service

Dr. Stadter has psychiatric responsibility for the Lodge residents. He prescribes all psychotropic medication, giving the resident a prescription for a month's supply at a time, which he then obtains from the Fort Logan pharmacy. At a given time anywhere from half to three quarters of the residents are taking psychoactive drugs. Each man keeps his own supply.

If the residents should decide that a particular member needs to be rehospitalized, Dr. Stadter makes the arrangements. He does not pay any scheduled visits to the Lodge and is only rarely called in an emergency. In case of serious physical illness or emergencies, the Lodge members themselves arrange for the member to be taken to one of the local general hospitals. More routine physical problems are handled by Dr. Stadter through the Fort Logan medical clinic.

Outcome

The effectiveness of the Lodge as a means of enabling men with long history of serious mental illness to stay out of the hospital is being studied under a two-year grant[2] awarded by the National Institute of Mental Health in January 1969. A research team is studying the therapeutic climate, transactions, communication systems, and other internal processes, as well as gathering more complete outcome data on the residents' continuing community adjustment. A series of 21 questionnaires and interview schedules is being employed.

At the end of its first year of operation, half of the original residents were still living at the Lodge—a successful outcome in terms of the principal goal of keeping the men productive in a setting outside the hospital. Fort Logan feels, however, that the Lodge can be shown to have exerted a favorable influence on those who did not remain. The average stay for those who left during the first year was a little more than eight months. During that time, the men worked an average of 90 percent of the weeks they were in the Lodge.

For those who comprised the resident group in mid-1969, the average percentage of weeks worked was 96 percent. Said a Fort Logan report:

> The meaning of these figures emerges when one considers the work record of this group during the year prior to their entering the Lodge: eight of them did not work at all in the community, three of them worked three or four weeks, two a total of about nine weeks, one about

---

[2] National Institute of Mental Health Grant #1-R 01-MH 15853-01.

40 weeks. One suffering from brain damage had never worked in his life until he entered the Lodge; there he worked 79 of his 102 weeks in the program.

During the six months prior to this year-end report, the men had earned $298 each, which compares favorably with the zero income of eight of them and the $50 earned by two others during the six months prior to entering the Lodge.

> In this . . . tally [the report continued] it may be fitting to consider the Lodge from the standpoint of the taxpayer. At the present time it costs $3.50 a day to maintain a man in the Lodge. This cost compares with . . . 24-hour care at about $35 per day, outpatient care, about $8 a visit. . . . In addition to its demonstrated benefits to the members, the Lodge is saving the taxpayer money. If, in time, the Lodge concept can be made available to 100 of the state's chronic, 24-hour patients, the savings could be on the order of . . . approximately $1,150,000 per year.[3]

Agency and community relationships

The excellent relationship between the Lodge and those most directly associated with it at Fort Logan has been described, but it is not in fact accurate to characterize this as either an agency or a community relationship. Despite the fact that the Lodge is functionally a nearly autonomous agency, that it has its own board, and that the hospital has deliberately chosen to play a nonauthoritative role, nonetheless the Lodge is the brainchild of Fort Logan and, we believe, dependent on the backup services of Fort Logan in order to survive as a viable program. At the same time it should be noted that within Fort Logan there have been some distinct pockets of resistance. Some staff members were alarmed that no staff coverage was planned for evenings and weekends. Some were concerned that the program did not include such "necessities" as group therapy. Certain of the Fort Logan treatment teams are still reluctant to make referrals to the Lodge.

An important agency relationship is that with the Colorado Division of Rehabilitation, which makes a fee-for-service payment of $220 per month for each man, up to a maximum of 18 months. (This is the

---

[3] No better example of the spiraling costs of health care could be found than these figures for mid-1969, when compared with the costs as of mid-1970. The cost of maintaining a man in the Lodge has risen to about $5 per day, while the cost of inpatient care at Fort Logan has risen to about $50 per day. Using these more recent figures, the tax savings available from the Lodge type of program become even more substantial.

longest period of support possible under the federal vocational rehabilitation regulations; Colorado is one of the few states that have elected to participate in this "extended evaluation" service available only to the mentally ill and the mentally retarded.)

The business manager described some minor difficulties with labor unions that were concerned about competition for jobs. In each case he has been able to negotiate these complaints successfully.

There has been no difficulty at all with neighbors in the relatively anonymous neighborhood in which the Lodge is located.

Financing

The Lodge has existed mainly on the funds described above from the Colorado Division of Rehabilitation—$125 per month for room and board, plus $95 per month for the rehabilitative services. A few of the present residents have already exceeded the 18-month period of support permitted by the Division of Rehabilitation, and their cases have therefore been closed.

The residents also contribute to the cost of running the house. By rule of the house, each man is permitted to keep the first $30 of each month's earnings, but is required to contribute one half of everything else he earns. The hope is that eventually there can be sufficient work for each man to earn his full room and board.

Because of the difficulty of finding suitable premises which the landlord would be willing to rent for this particular purpose, the Lodge agreed to pay $50 per man per month for rent. Considering the quality of the accommodations, this seemed to us extortionate.

Future plans

There seems to be complete consensus among the people we talked with—Fort Logan staff members, including the director, the research staff assigned under the NIMH grant, and Colorado's chief of mental health in the Department of Institutions—that the Lodge program is a setting-of-choice for certain long-term patients who have inadequate vocational histories and difficulties in managing their lives outside a hospital. They all agreed that several more such programs, including one or more for women, would be useful in their state. Subsequent to our visit plans were developed for starting a Lodge for women, hopefully by the end of 1970. Also, arrangements were worked out with Denver General Hospital and the Veterans Administration Hospital whereby they will be able to refer their patients to the Lodge.

X. Cobble Hill Center
Brooklyn

NAMED FOR THE GEOGRAPHIC SECTION OF BROOKLYN in which it is located, Cobble Hill Center is one of the country's few privately owned community residence facilities for the mentally ill, and one of the largest.

Origins

Cobble Hill Center came into being through the interest and efforts of Dr. Karl Easton, who in the mid-1960's was assigned by the New York City Community Mental Health Board as the first psychiatric consultant to the city's welfare department. He soon learned that out of about 15,000 state hospital patients then being released to New York City each year, about 5,000 applied to the welfare department for funds to live on. A large percentage ended up living in substandard residential hotels, largely clustered on the Upper West Side of Manhattan. The readmission rate to the state hospitals was extremely high among these patients—75 percent within a year. Dr. Easton carried out a study of his own, wherein he followed up 100 patients, and found that half of them were rehospitalized within three months. He became convinced that many of these people would be able to remain in the community if a professionally supervised residential facility with an active program were available to them.

In 1966 he learned of a large building that had previously housed a YWCA but had stood vacant during the two years since the YWCA had moved to its newer building a few blocks away.

Dr. Easton worked out an arrangement with the welfare department whereby it would pay $25 per week per resident for rent—$5 more than the standard figure, with the differential covering the cost of the supervision and activities program that he proposed to provide at Cobble Hill. He then formed a private corporation which leased the building for five years, with an option to buy. He undertook some fairly extensive renovation which was necessary to make the building adequate for his purposes. He notified the welfare department and the eight state hospitals serving the New York City area of the availability of Cobble Hill, and at the end of February 1967 the first residents arrived. Within a year all of the two hundred beds were filled. For some time there has been a waiting list that runs from two to three months.

A few months later, a separate nonprofit corporation was formed to establish a vocational rehabilitation institute to provide vocational evaluation, training, counseling, and placement. To qualify for support from the New York State Division of Vocational Rehabilitation, this institute, located on the ground floor of Cobble Hill, has been open to persons outside the residence, although the majority of its clients are in fact Cobble Hill residents.

Physical facilities

Cobble Hill Center is located in a solidly constructed eight-story building in a principally commercial and industrial section of Brooklyn. The neighborhood is substantially anonymous. Subway and bus transportation are readily accessible.

The ground floor, with a reception desk and individual mailboxes for the residents, gives the appearance of a small hotel lobby. One side contains a large, well-furnished, and carpeted lounge area where paintings by the residents are on display, and where there is a color television set. Across the lobby are the offices of the vocational rehabilitation institute. There are also a few rooms for residents on this floor.

In the basement there are several areas set aside for painting, sewing, and various other arts and crafts.

The second through the sixth floors contain the rest of the rooms for the 180 women and 20 men residents. All are single rooms, each about seven by twelve feet. Those that we saw were neat and clean, and most had been personalized by the addition of photographs, prints, souvenirs, and so on. Each room has a bed, a dresser, and a closet.

Each resident has a key to his room; the staff members have master keys, and they do not hesitate to enter a resident's room if they have any reason to believe that all is not well with him. Each floor has two large central bathrooms. The corridors are carpeted and clean, and the walls freshly painted.

The seventh floor contains a kitchen, a cafeteria serving line, and colorful and attractive dining tables and chairs. The eighth floor houses the laundry facilities and storage and recreational areas.

The staff

The professional staff consists of Dr. Easton; a general director, who has a master's degree in social work; an art therapist; and one floor counselor, who is a psychiatric nurse. In our interviews with these people, they impressed us as sharing a therapeutic approach that can best be described as kind firmness, intended to bring reality into view at all times. As a group they appeared to be forthright and honest but not alarmingly directive with their residents. They seemed to be clear on what is appropriate behavior, about how to work together, about their own limitations. We found them open and direct, not hesitating to correct each other or to offer alternative views.

They showed an amazing awareness of the problems of each of their two hundred residents. As we walked about the building, residents frequently stopped the staff members to ask some question, and the staff were fully acquainted with the residents' circumstances and problems. In each case they offered encouragement, and oftentimes direct suggestions. While the staff are fully aware of the status of their residents in terms of their histories of hospitalization in state hospitals, nonetheless they treat the residents as if they were "not mentally ill," for the purpose of reducing or eliminating any gains that might come from being considered ill and to discourage inappropriate behavior.

Dr. Easton, with the title of consultant, spends about fifteen hours per week on the premises. He spends the rest of his time as chief of psychiatry for a nearby hospital and seeing a few private patients. He is a board-certified psychiatrist and child psychiatrist and a certificated mental hospital administrator. We found him an impressive man with much energy, many creative ideas, and the courage to move ahead with them.

The general director of Cobble Hill is Irving Link, a social worker who worked as assistant to Dr. Easton while he was with the welfare department. He impressed us as well informed, articulate, and sensitive, and an excellent person to collaborate with Dr. Easton and to implement their ideas. He seemed to have organized the operation of Cobble Hill with a great deal of skill and self-confidence.

Both the general director and Dr. Easton consider themselves to be "on call" 24 hours a day, and frequently they are called after hours. Either or both usually drop in on weekends to make themselves available. Mr. Link also holds "open doors" hours each afternoon, at which time any of the two hundred residents who want to discuss a problem with him may come in without an appointment; between ten and twenty residents avail themselves of this opportunity each afternoon.

Dr. Easton's wife is also on the full-time staff. With training in art education, she initially joined the staff intending only to teach art. As it turned out, she has been deeply involved in a great many of the developing components of the program. For example, she played a major role in creating the food service department, which, through the vocational rehabilitation unit, prepares and serves meals for the residents and provides training experiences in Personal Adjustment Training as well as evaluation opportunities.

We interviewed the floor counselor who had been on the job only a few weeks. With a master's degree in psychiatric nursing, she came to Cobble Hill from a supervisory position at one of the state hospitals. She took a cut in pay in order to get into a job where she could once more have substantial contact with patients. Cobble Hill plans eventually to have a counselor for each of the six residential floors; at the time of our visit, this young nurse was the only such counselor. She was still in process of getting to know the residents, but had already involved herself with a number of them in assisting with particular problems. For example, she was helping one resident with diabetes management and several others with handling their funds from the welfare department. She occasionally mediates interpersonal disputes, and she sees some residents individually concerning their emotional problems. Her working hours are 1 to 9 p.m., in order to allow her to be present during the early evening hours, when the majority of residents are on the premises.

Other staff members include a needlecraft instructor, an office manager, and maintenance, housekeeping, and office staff. For vocational training there are three rehabilitation counselors available through the vocational rehabilitation institute as well as two cooks and a dietitian.

The residents

Cobble Hill compiled statistical data about its residents as of May 31, 1969, or 27 months after its opening. During that time there had been 603 different residents, of whom 394 had been discharged. Those residents who were returned to state hospitals made up 36 percent of the discharges; this compares with a relapse rate of 75 percent among the general mental hospital population returning from New York City to the state hospitals within one year after discharge.

While Cobble Hill asserts that it accepts all categories of the mentally ill, in actuality almost all residents have had a diagnosis of schizophrenia. About 90 percent of them came directly from state hospitals, the other ten percent from the community. The average number of hospitalizations was 2.8; 71 percent of the residents had undergone one, two, or three hospitalizations and 29 percent had been hospitalized from four to twelve times.

The average age for the total group was 36 years. Almost half—43 percent—had never been married. The distribution by religious persuasion shows 36 percent Protestants, 33 percent Catholics, 25 percent Jewish, and a smattering of others. By race, exactly three quarters are white, 19 percent are Negroes, and the rest are scattered. The average education of all residents was slightly over eleven years.

Of all those discharged from Cobble Hill, the average stay had been just under six months. However, it was longer—7.3 months—for those who were discharged to take up autonomous living in the community than for those who were returned to hospital (5.1 months). There is no limit on length of stay, and of those residing in the house as of the end of May 1969, about half had been there longer than a year.

Because there is a waiting list at Cobble Hill, the intake procedure is lengthy. When a state hospital staff member has a patient that he believes is a good candidate, he calls for an appointment. In the meantime, a summary of the patient's history is prepared by the hospital and sent to Cobble Hill. Then when a vacancy is about to become available, the prospective resident comes in for an interview with Dr. Easton, Mr. Link, and sometimes other members of the staff. The hospital social worker usually accompanies the patient. At this time an intake form is completed, and if the applicant is accepted, it is perhaps another month before he can be admitted to the center. It may well be that this long-drawn-out procedure constitutes a powerful selection process in itself.

About ten percent of the referrals are rejected, because they are acutely psychotic, or pose difficult management problems, or, most important, because they have other appropriate resources available to them in the community. Mr. Link and Dr. Easton readily acknowledge that they cannot predict which patients will do best, although it is their impression (as at some of the other programs) that the long-term chronically ill patients do better than the younger and more acutely ill patients; that is to say, the longer-term patients seem to stay out of the hospital longer and require less staff attention while they are at Cobble Hill.

Cobble Hill accepts patients with controlled seizures; approximately ten percent of their residents are on antiepileptic medication.

Putatively there are both a lower age limit (18) and an upper age limit (55), but they are not strictly adhered to.

Substantially all of the residents who come from the state hospitals have been discharged outright and are not on any form of conditional or convalescent leave. Patients may come to Cobble Hill from any of New York's state hospitals, but those who relapse and require rehospitalization may go only to Kings Park State Hospital, which serves the catchment area in which Cobble Hill is located.

Dr. Easton described the residents as "almost without exception having very little self-confidence about anything, including their bodies. For example, one will get a cold and experience a great deal more anxiety than ordinary people would. They are frightened people who fear many things."

As we toured the facility and chatted with the residents, we were persuaded that Cobble Hill serves the most chronic category of patients that are discharged from state hospitals—people who are troubled and limited in many ways in their capabilities to live autonomously outside the hospital.

The program

The philosophy of the Cobble Hill program seems to be approximately as follows. Because many of the people who have been in state hospitals are unable to go directly from the hospital to self-support, they must rely on particular support resources if they are to be enabled to stay out of the hospital. Using funds primarily from welfare, the program provides physically clean housing and decent food along with a milieu that allows an indefinite period of adjustment and adaptation in the community. The basic goal is to prevent rehospitalization, with secondary goals of economic and social rehabilitation.

Expectation is the keystone. Said Dr. Easton:

> We take the position that nobody living here is sick. When we first opened up, everybody acted sick. People would regress, and their rooms would be filthy, and they wouldn't have social graces. When we asked them why they were behaving like this, they would say, "Look, we're sick, we're mental patients." Things reached the point that we were forced to a different approach. We took the position that if you're mentally ill or if you act mentally ill then you belong in a hospital, and you can't continue to live here because we can't take it. We stopped using the term "halfway house" because it encouraged the sickness role. We point out that they've been discharged and are therefore not mental patients. We use this as a club. This really positive approach is our main concept.

The mood of Cobble Hill is one in which residents come and go rather freely. They have access to vocational, social, and recreational activities, and seem free to choose whatever counseling or aftercare services they may feel useful (if any). On a given day, about half of the 200 residents are absent from Cobble Hill, either at work or in school, or otherwise engaged in the community. Of the other 100, about 35 can be found isolated in their rooms; the remaining 65 are occupied in one way or another in the activities at Cobble Hill.

The schedule of activities available within the center is impressive. The needlecraft shop is open from nine to three every day of the week. The art studio is open for several hours a day Monday through Friday. There are weekly card parties, dancing, song sessions, bingo, knitting classes, a "longhairs club," a poetry group, a creative expression class, a chess and checkers club, music appreciation, and several other group events. Each week there are orientation sessions for new residents, a meeting of the residents with Dr. Easton, a resident government meeting, and an employment and rehabilitation meeting. There is no charge for any of the activities except a modest fee for the weekly swimming party at the nearby YWCA.

There is no curfew in the evening, although the doors are locked at 10 p.m. to keep strangers out. Individual curfews are sometimes imposed for particular reasons, usually in the case of residents who seem to lack sufficient control over their actions or to be confused. In rare cases a kind of "house detention" is imposed for a resident who particularly needs structure; he may be required to stay within the facility for as long as a week at a time.

The resident government activities, initiated a short time before our visit, are intended to be an important part of the Cobble Hill milieu. Each floor elects a floor chairman, an assistant floor chairman, a welcoming chairman, a bulletin board committee representative, and two floor representatives, all of whom represent each floor at a weekly meeting of the resident government. Each floor also holds its own meeting every week. There is a president of the resident government, and he attends the weekly staff meeting of the professional staff.

Certain cliques exist within the house. Sometimes these are ethnic in nature, as when a group of women of Italian extraction spend an evening together at an Italian restaurant. More often they develop according to age, with residents tending to socialize with fellow residents of their own age group. There do not seem to be any groupings according to hospitalization experience, illness, or particular deficits or handicaps.

Residents may receive visitors in the common rooms downstairs, but may not entertain in their rooms, except occasionally when families come to visit. Drinking is forbidden on the premises, and a person who violates this rule will be reprimanded, although not expelled unless he persists. Residents are also required to treat each other with courtesy and respect. "We don't allow people to be mean to other people or to behave unpleasantly," Dr. Easton said.

THE VOCATIONAL REHABILITATION INSTITUTE has a capacity of about forty, in three different programs—a seven-week evaluation and two Personal Adjustment Training programs, one clerical, the other kitchen work. At the time of our visit there were 26 people participating in the rehabilitation program, all but four of them residents of Cobble Hill. The major emphases of the institute seem to be on punctuality, motivation to work, and work habituation. The prospective client is referred to the Division of Vocational Rehabilitation where a counselor determines whether he should be accepted. If he is, he then undergoes the evaluation program of testing, group and individual counseling, and simulated job trials. At the end of the evaluation he may either go out to find a job if he is considered capable of doing so, or he may be admitted to one of the Personal Adjustment Training programs, which run for a twelve-week period with extensions up to 36 weeks. We were told that of the ninety percent who successfully complete the Personal Adjustment Training, the majority are not equipped at the end of it to go into full-time competitive employment, although many are capable of taking part-time jobs. (Cobble Hill itself provides some wage-earning opportunities for its members, with as many as fifteen at a time working from one and a half to two hours per day in a variety of activities around the facility.) Occasionally a person who has completed the Personal Adjustment Training program is then referred to DVR for more formal skill training in a regular outside training facility. There is not much effort within the rehabilitation institute on recruiting jobs with employers who would be willing to hire people with a history of mental illness. In view of the fact that only about twenty percent of the residents are working full time and another fifteen percent part time, it seemed to us that it would be a useful service to the residents if there were an expansion of staff that would allow time to contact prospective employers.

THE PROGRAM AT COBBLE HILL CENTER is the most extensive among the eleven facilities that we visited. It can be considered still in the formative stage, since it is only a little over three years old and has been struggling financially. In the event that more generous funding should become available, the center will augment its staff so as to be able to involve its members more actively in the program. In the meantime, its emphasis both on enhancing psychosocial skills and the ability to work is impressive. Even though the staff do not have high expectations for certain of the residents, they clearly expect some progress from them and treat them accordingly.

Medication and medical service

It was interesting to us that Cobble Hill Center on the one hand has more psychiatric participation than all except one other of the eleven programs we visited, and on the other hand attaches little importance to psychotropic medication. Dr. Easton acknowledges that medication is important for particular individuals, and he has sometimes urged patients who were beginning to behave bizarrely to return to the source from which they obtain their medications. But for the most part he feels that state hospital patients have been overmedicated, that the dosages given in community treatment facilities are also often too high, and that many of the ex-patients can function satisfactorily with no medication at all. Frequently he has advised residents to reduce the dosage they have been taking.

A state-run aftercare clinic is located only about four blocks from Cobble Hill Center. About half the residents go there to obtain new supplies of medication. Dr. Easton feels that the service is rarely individualized and that there is a considerable tendency just to fill a bottle with tablets or capsules without any meaningful determination of the individual's specific medication needs at the particular time.

Physical health needs of the residents are largely met by a general practitioner in the vicinity. He is willing to make calls at Cobble Hill on patients who are too ill to come to his office. Most of the residents he sees from Cobble Hill are covered for fees under Medicaid.

Outcome

It is important to keep in mind that Cobble Hill Center does not consider itself a *transitional* residence for many of the people who come there to live. While there seems to be at all times a push towards self-sufficiency, no time limit is set for the residents, and indeed a given individual would presumably be welcome to stay for the rest of his life. At the time of our visit, about half of the residents had been living at Cobble Hill for more than a year.

Even so, there is considerable movement outward. Of approximately 140 residents who presently leave Cobble Hill each year, about one fourth leave to return to hospital.

Unfortunately, Cobble Hill has not undertaken any sort of follow-up study to ascertain the outcome for its residents after they have moved to autonomous living arrangements in the community. Its information is limited to each patient's status as of the day he terminated his relationship with Cobble Hill. As a proprietary facility operating on a tight budget, Cobble Hill has had no mandate or obligation to do such a study, but because of the important model that it represents, one can hope that it will find the means to do so in the future. In the meantime, very limited records are kept on the residents even while they live at Cobble Hill; after each new resident's four-week orientation period has expired, one of the staff writes a summary report, but otherwise there are no records.

Dr. Easton and Mr. Link do not have any ready explanation of why certain patients fail and others succeed. They note that residents who return to hospital often do so on their own initiative, particularly on weekends. They feel that some of those who return to hospital had been released prematurely, while others want to return because they miss the ties they had established there. Of those who are sent back on the initiative of Cobble Hill, in most cases it is a matter of an acute psychotic episode that renders the resident unmanageable. Some of these, instead of returning directly to the state hospital, go to Kings County Hospital, the receiving hospital for Brooklyn, where they are evaluated; in a few cases of prompt remission, the patients have been returned from this general hospital to Cobble Hill rather than being transferred to the state hospital.

When a resident seems ready to move to his or her own private living quarters, Cobble Hill sometimes helps by calling one of the residential hotels that it considers superior in its price range. Otherwise the residents usually find their own apartments through classified newspaper advertisements.

The Cobble Hill staff do not know how many of its former residents who move on to autonomous living arrangements subsequently relapse and return to hospital. They know that some do, since word gets to them either from the hospital staff or from residents who are friends of the rehospitalized persons. Dr. Easton does not believe that rehospitalization in all cases represents a failure. "We hear of people who had been hospitalized for a year before they come to us, and then when they return to the state hospital they stay a much shorter time, often no more than two or three months," he told us. "Rehospitalization in some cases must be viewed as a step in the process of getting better."

Only a few of the former residents return to Cobble Hill Center to visit or to take part in activities, and there is no special program for them.

About 85 percent of the residents who move into apartments remain on welfare rolls, with only about 15 percent working even part time. The staff attribute this low vocational success rate to *a*) severe problems in motivation, together with a high anxiety level and a poor ability to conform to work group norms, *b*) the negative incentive effect of the welfare scale, and *c*) too brief periods of Personal Adjustment Training allowed by the Division of Vocational Rehabilitation. We were told that many of these clients are suitable for long-term sheltered workshop employment but that no such facilities exist in New York City; all of the workshops there are organized as short-term transitional services.

Agency and community relationships

Cobble Hill appears to have relatively few relationships with outside agencies, and all of these appear to be successful. Service from the vocational rehabilitation counselors has ranged from moderately to highly satisfactory, depending on the particular counselor serving the facility at a given time. Relationships with the state hospitals have been at least sufficiently satisfactory for Cobble Hill to run a two- to three-month waiting list at all times. The attitude of the city welfare department is indicated by its agreement to pay a small "premium" to Cobble Hill in order to cover part of the costs of providing the recreational and social activities.

There have been no problems at all with neighbors.

Financing

The considerable majority of the funds coming in to Cobble Hill consists of payments from the welfare department, which every two weeks sends a check for each resident in the amount of $122. Of this, $99 goes to Cobble Hill to cover the room, breakfasts, dinners, and the social and recreational program. Thus the client keeps $23 each two weeks to cover personal expenses. The amount paid to Cobble Hill comes to about $7 per resident per day, not including lunch. This compares with an expenditure of $16 per day for patients in state hospitals in New York.

For the relatively few residents—usually about 25 at a time—who are participating in the activities of the rehabilitation institute, the Division of Vocational Rehabilitation pays Cobble Hill a fee of $40 per week to cover the training, and the client an additional $10.50 a week to cover the cost of lunch.

Future plans

Cobble Hill Center, at the time of our visit, was in process of applying for approval as a "proprietary home for adults" under the provisions of the New York State Department of Social Services. This new status would increase the compensation per resident by about $120 per month (but would also require that a third meal be served each day). A principal reason for wanting this reclassification is the funds that it would make available to hire more staff members. We have already mentioned that Cobble Hill wants very much to have a floor counselor for each of its six residential floors. Dr. Easton and Mr. Link would like additional professional staff to expand the program and to provide greater opportunities for interaction between the residents and staff who would serve as role models.

The authors can appreciate the intention of Cobble Hill in applying for this new classification; there seems no question that the quite small staff is carrying a tremendous workload with which it keeps abreast only by means of exceptional investment in and dedication to the value of the work. At the same time, we could not help feeling twinges of disappointment, precisely because the Cobble Hill program seemed to be accomplishing its goals effectively and inexpensively. This is much in contrast with the "psychiatric hotels" that have been started in several cities as a means of emptying out long-term chronic patients from the state hospitals into old hotels that have no mental health staff and no program whatever.

In any case, the accomplishments of Cobble Hill Center to date are sufficiently impressive as to bring into question the concept of halfway houses limited to no more than fifteen or twenty residents. This small size may turn out to be the most effective in many cases. But the Cobble Hill experience indicates that it is possible to provide a kind, supportive, humane, inexpensive, and large program in the community for people who have a history of mental illness.

XI. Transitional Care Program
Elgin State Hospital
Chicago and Elgin, Illinois

THROUGH A FOUR-PHASE PROGRAM, designed to begin on the state hospital grounds and end up with autonomous living in a large city, the Transitional Care Program of Elgin State Hospital provides a highly developed effort to effect the release and successful reintegration into community life of long-term, dependent patients who, without this special support, show essentially no potential for life outside the hospital.

Origins

Elgin State Hospital, a facility that receives patients from certain portions of metropolitan Chicago, has reduced its inpatient census over the years from a high of 6965 to a figure in mid-1970 of 2938. Among the current census are hundreds of long-term patients who are considered to be deeply institutionalized and "industrialized"; that is, adjusted to and successfully performing in a hospital work program but with little evident potential for being able to sustain the work pattern outside the structured environment of the hospital.

In 1965 the hospital submitted to the National Institute of Mental Health a proposal requesting Hospital Improvement Project grant funds for a three-year period to establish a special "re-entry" program that would afford such patients special preparation for discharge. The grant was approved in mid-1966, and the hospital thereupon assigned two cottages on the hospital grounds—one for men and one for women—to be developed as a "quarterway house" that would carry out the first phase of the rehabilitation program. In October 1966 the first patients moved in.

Concurrently the search began for a physical plant for a halfway house in Chicago to which the patients successfully completing the quarterway house program could move on. Almost a year was required to find an acceptable facility, and there were further delays because of snags in state purchasing procedures for the furnishings. Consequently, for a short time the Chicago-based halfway house had to place its residents in a residential hotel, while operating only a day program. Then in September 1967 the halfway house, known as Roscoe House after the street on which it is located, began full operation. The program was financed with federal funds until the grant expired in mid-1969, and since then has been supported from the budget of Elgin State Hospital.

Physical facilities

The first phase takes place on the hospital grounds in two small, red-brick cottages formerly occupied by employees. A total of 28 residents are housed: 14 men and 14 women. The semiprivate rooms are furnished with beds, dressers, night stands, lamps, and chairs.

Although the cottages are technically wards they have never been locked. Residents have keys to their own rooms and individual closets.

The staff offices and group rooms are interspersed with resident rooms, enhancing staff-resident interaction and reducing the opportunity for withdrawal.

The buildings are perceived as one structure during the day as residents and staff mix together in cooking, cleaning, discussions, and recreation. In the basement of one cottage are the kitchen and dining room (groceries are received from the hospital dietary department but meals are prepared by rotating resident committees). The area has been decorated by the residents with curtains, tablecloths, and rugs. The other basement area serves as the indoor recreation and lounge area and houses the residents' washer and dryer.

The relationship with the hospital is "both independent and dependent." Like other wards, the cottages receive basic supplies, equipment, and some services such as linens. Unlike other wards, the residents do their own cooking and dishwashing, personal laundry, yard work, and housekeeping.

Roscoe House is located on the Near North Side of Chicago in a middle- to lower-middle-class neighborhood whose residents are primarily native Caucasians, although with some Puerto Ricans and Negroes. The house is a former apartment building that contains twelve small apartments, four each on three floors. Those on the first floor are used as office space and group meeting rooms; the remaining eight, on the second and third floors, are used for the residents. Each apartment will accommodate three men or women, although when the house is operating at less than capacity the residents are assigned so that some apartments have only two people. Each has a small living room, a small bedroom, a kitchen, and a bath. The bedroom is fitted out with bunk beds, and the third resident sleeps on a sofa bed in the living room.

The furnishings, ordered by the state, are modest and institutional in appearance. Although valiant efforts seem to have been made by residents and staff to make both the apartments and the offices attractive and comfortable, one must say that this old-fashioned, fairly run-down building and its accouterments are only marginally adequate.

At the time of our visit some beginning efforts had been made to decorate and renovate the unfinished basement so as to make it usable for serving meals on special occasions, for meetings of the resident group, etc.

The Transitional Care Program staff had great difficulty in finding any facility at all that would serve its purposes. The present building became available largely because the rent was guaranteed from public funds and because the program agreed that the tenants would provide certain maintenance, such as painting. As a result the landlord has declined to carry out some of the most rudimentary maintenance and repairs. The program pays a high rent.

Roscoe House is convenient to shopping and public transportation.

The staff

The first director of the Transitional Care Program was Robert Geigner, a social worker who was subsequently promoted to be Elgin State Hospital's director for its "Subzone Eight," the geographic area which the Transitional Care Program serves. His assistant, Kenneth Karrels, a psychologist with a master's degree, was promoted to the job of director of aftercare for Subzone Eight. In this capacity he spends approximately equal amounts of time supervising the quarterway house at Elgin, the halfway house in Chicago, and a separate and unrelated program under which more dependent elderly patients who need more structure are placed in foster homes and boarding homes in Chicago.

All employees of Transitional Care are state civil service employees assigned to the payroll of Elgin State Hospital. There is an authorized strength of twenty for the quarterway house, including trainees and students, although at the time of our visit it was greatly understaffed, with eight vacancies. These include a mental health program worker, a nurse supervisor, an MSW social worker, two psychologists trained at the master's level, a workshop manager, a housekeeper, a social work trainee, a psychology intern, an "institutional worker," and seven aides.

Roscoe House has an authorized staff of eleven, including two field-work students from the University of Chicago School of Social Work; there were two vacancies at the time of our visit. The principal staff member is an MSW social worker, who as part of his responsibilities supervises a social work supervisor who in turn supervises four bachelor's-level social workers and an activity therapist, who carry out most of the case management both for the present residents and for a considerably larger number of alumni—between eighty and one hundred—who have moved on to independent living arrangements in the community. There are also a rehabilitation counselor and a vocational instructor; there were vacancies for a nurse and a clerk-typist.

The social work supervisor and the Roscoe House director each carry a small caseload. Most of the residents and ex-residents are assigned to the four bachelor's-level staff members. At a given time each of these social workers may have a caseload of three to six "Phase II" residents (those living in Roscoe House) and fifteen to thirty "Phase III" residents (those who have moved on to community living arrangements). All of these are seen regularly, typically once a week but ranging from daily to once a month. In addition, the staff members are on constant call in event of emergency. One social worker told us that she averages about three evening calls per week and that she finds it necessary to drive in from her home at night perhaps twice a month to see one of her clients.

The Roscoe House staff members were awe-inspiring in their dedication to their work and to the welfare of the people entrusted to them. Each worker develops a supportive and encouraging relationship with each person on his caseload. The focus is on helping the individual to acquire sufficient social, vocational, and personal skills to enable him to live in the community. The worker may teach the resident how to talk to an employer, how to manage his money, how to apply for welfare funds, how to shop, how to care for his apartment. If a woman is afraid of the kitchen, a social worker will help her cook a meal. If a man is afraid to go downtown alone on the bus, the psychologist will accompany him the first time, rather than talk about feelings from behind a desk. The caseworkers handle arrangements to get clients into vocational training programs. They go to the clinic with clients who have medication problems. The orientation of the staff, in other words, seems to be toward the here and now, toward the belief that the immediate everyday actions, reactions, and interpersonal relationships are the essentials of therapeutic progress. Because the staff have found that many residents cannot meaningfully interact among themselves well enough to allow for a successful therapeutic community, staff-resident transactions are largely on an individual basis.

The staff feel that formal training is relatively unimportant. Said John Cunningham, the Roscoe House director, "The bachelor's-level people function extremely well; they're a lot more competent than many people give them credit for."

There are three one-hour staff meetings each week. One is devoted to a review of the second-floor residents, another to the third-floor residents, and the third to certain group activities (described below) in which most of the residents and some ex-residents are involved.

Some staff members seemed to regret that a good deal of time was taken up with maintenance and housekeeping matters that might better be handled by a housekeeper and/or maintenance man, if there were such. Said the social work supervisor, "Unfortunately a lot of my time goes to keeping coal in the coalbin and patching broken windows."

The residents

The sole source of participants in the Transitional Care Program is the wards of Elgin State Hospital. The target population is the patient group *a*) who have been hospitalized for at least one year, *b*) whose symptoms are in reasonable remission, *c*) who are not suicidal or assaultive, *d*) who show some promise of being able, following preparation and with continuing support, to function at least semi-independently in the community, and *e*) who appear quite unlikely ever to be candidates for discharge without such special preparation and support.

The considerable majority are schizophrenics; most of these are diagnosed as chronic undifferentiated type, a smaller number as paranoid type. A few others are diagnosed as having manic-depressive psychosis Rarely are there referrals from any other diagnostic categories. Sex deviates, alcoholics, and the seriously retarded are deliberately excluded. The length of stay in the state hospital for those who entered the program in 1969 was ten years, with a range from one to 38 years.

There are more women than men—58 percent vs. 42 percent. Relatively few are currently married—21 percent of the women and only three percent of the men. Forty-eight percent of the women and 71 percent of the men have never been married, and 31 percent of the women and 26 percent of the men are divorced or separated.

There is no longer a provisional discharge or "convalescent leave" status in Illinois; all patients who leave state hospitals are discharged outright. Principally for this reason the Transitional Care Program does not accept anyone under 21. Among those who lived in Roscoe House in 1969, 19 percent were in their twenties; 27 percent were in their thirties; 22 percent were in their forties; 25 percent were in their fifties; and only seven percent were over 60 (the program has an upper age limit of 65).

The program

The Transitional Care Program has set forth the following assumptions that underlie its program:

- People are sent to mental hospitals because of behavior that falls outside the range of tolerance prescribed by social norms; thus, although the diagnosis may have psychiatric meaning, the expulsion from the community is related to social behavior.
- The "natural state is to be outside the hospital and inside the community."
- Behavior can change.
- An individual can function without necessarily having insight into his behavior.
- Low expectations support socially deviant behavior; as "normal" interaction is positively reinforced, appropriate behavior becomes internalized.
- Increased freedom (as at the quarterway house) requires increased responsibility, so that the past cannot be used as an excuse for present irresponsible behavior.

IF THERE WERE SUCH A THING AS AN IDEAL CLIENT for the Transitional Care Program, he would a) spend three months in the quarterway house (Phase I) followed by b) three months in Roscoe House (Phase II), followed by c) a move to some appropriate private living arrangement, while remaining active with Roscoe House for group activities and individual counseling (Phase III), followed by d) "alumni status" marked by complete separation from Roscoe House except for reunions or in the event an emergency should arise (Phase IV). Concurrently with Phases II and III, with such help from his counselor as he needs, he will have found a job or have qualified for some job-training program.

The clients do not, of course, obligingly follow this timetable. The three-month periods established for the quarterway house and for Roscoe House are goals that the program works toward rather than a limit that it imposes. A few quarterway house residents are transferred to Roscoe

House in less than three months, but a few take more than three months, occasionally staying six months or longer. The same is true of their stay at Roscoe House.

Within Elgin State Hospital there has been some resistance to providing referrals to the quarterway house, perhaps because of the skepticism with which new programs are frequently viewed. For this reason the Transitional Care Program staff have had to engage in a fairly constant process of drumming up business; by doing so they have kept the 28 beds full, or nearly so, most of the time. Once a patient moves to the quarterway house, he becomes known as a "resident." He has his own key to his own semiprivate room, where he keeps his personal effects.

In a structured program that covers from six and a half to seven hours a day, the quarterway house residents help to prepare meals and clean up afterward, take care of their own rooms, handle their own medications, and engage in a variety of planned activities. They attend two group therapy sessions a week and two staff-resident discussion groups, regarding problems in living together and the future. They are expected to work in the afternoon in a special sheltered workshop operated by the quarterway house, which has subcontracts from the hospital's central sheltered workshop. Interlaced with the above are planned and impromptu trips to the community for shopping, bowling, the movies, and so on, as well as periodic evening social gatherings between the two cottages that make up the quarterway house.

During his stay at the quarterway house, each resident makes three trips to Chicago to visit Roscoe House, and on one of these occasions stays overnight.

About one fifth of the patients who enter the quarterway house return to the hospital wards, usually within the first few weeks. Most leave because they feel the demands are greater than they can tolerate, others because they say they miss their friends back on the wards. Some need more structure. The expectancy level is too high for others. Of the twenty percent who return to the wards from the quarterway house, well over half are readmitted for a second chance. Many of these are successful the second time.

For the four fifths that are transferred to Roscoe House, readiness for the move is determined on the basis of individual performance in and response to the quarterway house preparation. On entering Roscoe House, each resident is assigned to one of the counselors and to an orientation group that meets three times a week for a two-week period.

There are a number of opportunities for group participation. For the Phase II residents who are unemployed, there are separate men's and women's "Outward Bound" groups which meet twice a week each; these sessions focus on the problems, fears, and feelings the members have in anticipation of moving to Phase III. For residents who are employed or are engaged in volunteer work at one of a variety of social agencies, there is an evening "community living" group. This group, which meets at Hull House, the famed settlement house, also involves some Phase III people, and focuses on social and employment problems.

There is a weekly meeting of all residents of Roscoe House, at which practical problems of house management are discussed. On another evening of the week there is a social group to which all Phase III people are invited, and which all Phase II residents are required to attend.

Two additional groups, both meeting at Hull House, are limited to Phase III members; one is for those who are unemployed, with membership terminating when a member begins work or a training program. The other is for those who have been away from Roscoe House for a longer period of time but need some continuing help in problem solving and social relationships. Other activities involve a group that meets weekly to prepare a newspaper, and a high school educational equivalency program, which are available both to Phase II and Phase III members.

P HASE III BEGINS when the individual "graduates" from Roscoe House, moving into an apartment, either alone or shared with another Roscoe House graduate, or a rooming house or boardinghouse, or one of the semisheltered psychiatric hotel facilities that exist in Chicago. While in Phase III, the member is still considered an active case but participates on an outpatient basis. He returns regularly, at an interval ranging from once a week to once a month, to meet with his counselor and discuss any adjustment problems that confront him, or to take part in some of the classes or discussion groups during the day or evening. If a client experiences difficulties during Phase III and seems to require closer supervision, he may return to Roscoe House until he seems able to return to his own living quarters.

About twenty Phase III members live in a single apartment building located about eight blocks from Roscoe House. We interviewed the manager of this building, an extraordinary woman who has become deeply involved with the Transitional Care Program. A former Roscoe House resident who came to live in this apartment building acquainted her with the program, and she paid the house a visit. With time she accepted more and more Roscoe House people, and at the time of our visit they were occupying 14 of the 78 apartments in her building. She finds them more satisfactory and less troublesome than her other tenants. They are quiet, don't have parties, don't drink excessively, and move less frequently.

She told us that about half of them were working, and some of the others were looking for work. A few attend sheltered workshops and a few can only do simple jobs such as baby sitting. Within the building they visit back and forth and go shopping together. Perhaps the strongest demonstration of her approval of the Roscoe House residents is the fact that she accepts them without a deposit, something she will not do for other people.

Phase IV represents alumni status, during which there is very little planned activity other than occasional reunions or open houses.

A^N IMPORTANT ASPECT OF THE ROSCOE HOUSE PROGRAM is that no staff reside there. During the first few months there was a live-in staff member, but when the program was being scrutinized in terms of budget problems, it was realized that he had so rarely been called upon to handle an emergency that the arrangement was ended. As we have said, residents have the telephone numbers of their counselors, but serious problems rarely arise during the off hours.

R OSCOE HOUSE PLACES LESS EMPHASIS NOW than it did initially on the need to be employed. Obviously it views employment as desirable and considers those who achieve employment as having the most successful outcome. But it also acknowledges that not all of the people who have been patients in a state hospital can become employed, and that for those it is preferable to be living in the community on welfare than to remain in the state hospital.

Residents sometimes locate their own jobs, with considerable support from their individual counselors. Some who seem unable to accept regular employment apply to the Division of Vocational Rehabilitation for sponsorship in a training program. These include a few members who are assigned to the Jewish Vocational Service and a rehabilitation center called Thresholds. A few do voluntary work for several local agencies, particularly the mental health association, a local general hospital, and a neighborhood nursery school. This program maintains more extensive records than most that we visited in this study. While the resident is in the quarterway house, duplicate case records are maintained, consisting of copies of social histories, psychological examinations, and any other significant information from the medical record, and progress notes written during the stay in the quarterway house. One copy is sent to Roscoe House about a month before the resident is to move there. While at Roscoe House a log of case contacts is kept, and a summary is prepared when the person moves away to his own living quarters. The log is continued throughout Phase III.

Medication and medical service

When a resident moves into Roscoe House he brings with him a month's supply of medication from the state hospital and a letter explaining his medication needs which he can present to any physician. Within about two weeks he receives a medical card from the welfare department which he can use to obtain medication without charge. Residents who are ineligible for welfare can obtain free medication from a Chicago State Hospital satellite clinic located about one and a half miles from Roscoe House.

The physicians who supervise the medication for the residents are for the most part general practitioners, many of whom were reported to be uneasy about prescribing heavy dosages of psychoactive drugs. We could not help wondering whether in some cases these dosages might best be reduced, since one cannot assume that the patient who was stabilized on drugs in the hospital environment will not require a change, or at least a review, of medication. Unfortunately, the Transitional Care Program budget does not provide for a psychiatric consultant for the Phase II and Phase III members. It seemed to us that a psychiatrist to oversee the medication of the members would be a useful and desirable addition to the program.

Outcome

Planning for the Transitional Care Program incorporated a formal research design under which there were to be two groups of state hospital patients of matched characteristics, one group to enter the four-phase program, the other to serve as a control group. In this manner, the efficacy of the special "re-entry" program could be reliably ascertained.

Unfortunately, many of the treatment staff of the wards from which the patients were to be referred grossly misunderstood the intention of the research effort. As they interpreted it, certain of their patients would be "controlled" by being retained in the hospital and denied any possibility of discharge. The Transitional Care Program staff found it impossible to dispel this misconception, and, as a result, there were no referrals at all from the wards. Consequently, it reluctantly abandoned the research plan.

We have mentioned that some of the quarterway house residents—about twenty percent—do not make it to Roscoe House on the first try. Of those who do, 34 percent are unable to function well enough to remain there and must be returned to the state hospital. In substantially all cases, these people are returned not to the wards from which they originated but to the quarterway house, in the hope that with some further preparation they will be ready to return to Roscoe House for a second try. About half of those returned to the quarterway house are subsequently transferred back to Roscoe House; the rate of success at Roscoe House for these "second tries" is about seventy percent.

The criteria of a successful outcome for those who leave Roscoe House have softened somewhat with time. Initially it was anticipated that the "successful" client would achieve both an autonomous living status and vocational independence. Neither of these goals is quite so much insisted upon now. Rather, the post-Roscoe House adjustment is considered successful even if the individual cannot work in the competitive market but must be supported by welfare payments, and even if his living arrangement turns out to be in a supervised setting, such as one of the psychiatric hotels. This shift in goals resulted from the Transitional Care Program staff's recognition and acceptance that some of their clients could live in the community but at a less than fully independent status, and a persuasion that even partial community living status is preferable to terminal residence in a state hospital.

About eighty percent of those who move on to Phase III—that is, leave Roscoe House other than to return to the hospital—go to some form of independent living, while the remaining twenty percent go to some other "sheltered" setting, such as one of the psychiatric hotels, or are re-established with their families. If a Phase III member should deteriorate in his community living arrangement, he can return to Roscoe House temporarily in the hope that he will restabilize there; about ten persons did return on this basis during 1969.

Among the Phase III members, about forty percent are in competitive employment or in a formal training program, while the remaining sixty percent live on welfare payments or Social Security disability benefits.

The program has found that older patients who have had a long and continuous hospitalization have responded more favorably than younger patients: older patients "who have made an adjustment to the hospital are far less volatile emotionally than younger people."

Agency and community relationships

Roscoe House seems to maintain effective, cooperative relationships with a variety of agencies in the Chicago area. It regularly refers members who seem candidates for competitive employment to the state employment service for direct job placement. Those needing job training are referred to the Division of Vocational Rehabilitation, which readily provides sponsorship. Members are accepted as clients by the Jewish Vocational Service workshop and Thresholds. The Mental Health Association of Greater Chicago frequently accepts residents in its clerical retraining program. Roscoe House residents participate in a variety of Hull House programs.

Some antagonism was expressed by the neighbors when they first learned of the purposes of Roscoe House. Several meetings were held, a group of the neighbors were invited to visit the quarterway house at the state hospital, and an open house was held at Roscoe House. The neighbors seem to have been won over.

Financing

Since the time the Hospital Improvement Project grant expired, all of the funds for operating the Transitional Care Program have come from the budget of Elgin State Hospital. During 1969 the total budget was about $215,000, almost equally split between the quarterway house and Roscoe House.

To determine the financial feasibility of the program, one would need more detailed and longer-term figures than are presently available. On the one hand, it seems slightly more expensive on a per diem basis to maintain a person in the quarterway house and Roscoe House than on the regular wards of the state hospital. On the other hand, the program is intended to be transitional, ideally with a stay of only three months each in the two residential components. As we have noted, the stay is sometimes longer, and not all of those who enter the program are successfully rehabilitated, nor are all of those who move on to community living gainfully employed; in fact, at this stage the majority continue to draw on public funds. Thus, the question of financial feasibility becomes one of how much appears to be saved in public money whenever an individual not only moves on to independent living but also becomes regularly employed. This program is dealing with people who, but for its special services, are not considered candidates for discharge from the hospital. Consequently, for each person with a thirty-year life expectancy who moves on to independent self-supporting living and remains in the community, the mental hospital may conceivably be saving more than $100,000, based on the current per diem expenditure. On this basis, one would need only a few "ideal outcomes" to justify the expense of the program.

XII. Gateways for Women
Gateways for Men
Indianapolis

G ATEWAYS FOR WOMEN was established in the late 1950's as one of the pioneering halfway houses in the United States, under the sponsorship of the Marion County Association for Mental Health. With a wealth of operating experience, it continues in much its original form; a second house, for men, was added in 1967.

Origins

In the late 1950's, the Marion County Association for Mental Health was in process of expanding from a small operation with a part-time staff to a broader, more comprehensive agency eventually to become one of the most active local mental health associations in the United States. Concurrently, its membership sought to identify a service component it might establish which would help to round out services locally available to the mentally ill. At this time there was a general ground swell of interest around the country in the plight of people who were being discharged from state hospitals, many after having been patients for many years. A rehabilitation committee appointed by the association investigated the halfway houses that had been established by Vermont's rehabilitation agency in conjunction with its state hospital, and Portals, a small, new halfway house in Los Angeles, and decided that this type of transitional residential facility would meet an important need for some of the patients being discharged to the Indianapolis area. The mental health association was being considered for membership in the local United Fund, and its application was approved to include the association itself, to provide the customary educational and advocacy functions, and the halfway house as a direct service to the mentally ill.

The house was established in the belief that "it is the experience and satisfaction of successfully coping with the social problems so often related to mental illness that ultimately determine the degree of complete rehabilitation after a patient's release from a psychiatric institution.

Success in solving problems related to employment, social adjustment, and self-independence . . . often decides the eventual success of the hospital treatment."

In the developmental stage, the mental health association's rehabilitation committee discussed its intentions with the directors of the two state hospitals in the county and with a number of other mental health professionals. While the professionals did not provide a great deal of impetus, they did greet the idea with a great deal of acceptance. A house in a (then) middle-class neighborhood in an intown area was located. Much of the furnishings were donated, particularly by members of the mental health association. Association funds were used to refurbish the house and to help defray initial operating expenses. In the spring of 1958 the first women came to live there.

Physical facilities

For almost a decade Gateways for Women remained at its original site, in a two-story frame house in an essentially anonymous intown section of Indianapolis. But during that time the neighborhood deteriorated drastically, and the residents, the staff, and the board of directors became increasingly concerned for the safety and security of the women living there.

In 1967 a new house was found, in a conveniently located and particularly attractive intown neighborhood, made up of large, well-built older homes set on spacious grounds.

The house was purchased for the program by the Indianapolis Foundation, which leases it back for one dollar per year; and it was refurbished with funds furnished by another local foundation, Lilly Endowment, Inc. Set well back from the street on attractive grounds, it is a three-story brick residence with a large front porch. All of the rooms are generous in size and gracious in appearance. The first floor has a living room, a den, an enclosed porch, a dining room, a well-equipped kitchen, and a suite for the housekeeper. The second floor has bedrooms accommodating a total of fourteen women in rooms for two and three. The third floor is used as a combination recreation-study area, with a sewing machine, typewriter, Ping-pong table, hair dryer, exercise machine, and ample storage space for residents' personal possessions. The furnishings throughout are attractive and harmonious; there is nothing whatever of the makeshift aspect of some halfway houses that we have seen.

The halfway house for men, rented for $100 per month, is located in the building that formerly housed the women's residence. Much less impressive in appearance, it needs refurbishing. This has not been done, however, because of the growing conviction that the program will have to abandon this location and find some new facility in a safer neighborhood of better quality. The United Fund itself is among those urging that a more desirable location be found.

The staff

The halfway houses have had the advantage of continuous direction from Norman Skole, a social worker by training, who has been the executive director of the Marion County Association for Mental Health since 1958. He allocates one fifth of his time to supervising the two social workers who have immediate responsibility for the halfway houses. Although he is consulted by them when special problems arise, his continuing role seems more one of general facilitation and support than of frequent and direct intervention or involvement in the day-to-day activities of the houses. It seems clear that he plays a major role in maintaining support for the houses both within the association and from a variety of professional agencies and individuals who are in one degree or another related to the houses.

The social work positions have turned over several times over the years. In earlier days these jobs were usually filled with people trained at the master's level. At present, both social workers have bachelor's degrees in psychology and no formal training in social work, although both have been employed on the social service staffs of state hospitals. While he has no prejudice against formally trained staff members, Mr. Skole has come to feel that personal characteristics may be at least as important as formal credentials. He described the attributes he sought for these jobs.

> . . . the right kind of personality, commitment, a willingness to dig in and work hard, a freedom from the need to be chained to a desk, a liberation from some of the more orthodox practices and attitudes of the past. I look for someone familiar with the other disciplines and with how a variety of community agencies operate. It's less important for the person to be an expert in the psychodynamics of mental illness than to be effective in dealing with the current reality problems and the current environment of the residents, and to be able to use effectively the backup from the doctors and social workers in the hospital.

The incumbents seemed to us to meet all of these requirements remarkably well. But Mr. Skole has found that in particular situations the current staff may require more frequent support than did the previous staff members trained at the master's level.

The social worker for the women's house, Mrs. Jean Hile, was for a time executive director of the mental health association in another county of Indiana; later, because she wanted to work directly with patients, she accepted a job on the social service staff of Logansport State Hospital. There she found that she missed the administrative aspects of her mental health association job. Thus, she accepted the current position as one that provides an ideal combination of patient contact and administrative responsibilities. At the time of our visit she had been with the program for a little more than a year.

The social worker for the men's house, Dale Schlabach, came to the men's halfway house about seven months prior to our visit.

Each starts the day with a visit to the house, spending up to three hours working with the housekeeper to deal with any problems that have arisen and seeing the residents in individual appointments. (Each resident is seen once a week, more often if necessary; those not available during these morning visits are seen in the late afternoon, or, if necessary, in the evening.) Each social worker conducts a weekly evening meeting of all the residents to discuss house problems.

After spending such time at the house as is necessary, each then goes to the offices of the mental health association. There they have responsibilities additional to the halfway houses; they operate the referral service which the association provides to all persons seeking information about any kind of mental health service. As regards the houses, they dictate reports, interview prospective residents, confer with a variety of agencies, and otherwise oversee a considerable amount of paper work that is part of the halfway house program, as described below.

Both social workers are on 24-hour call. Should the housekeeper encounter a problem that she feels she cannot handle, she will call the social worker. All of the residents have the home telephone numbers of the social workers, and each is free to telephone in the evening if he or she has a problem that will not seem to wait until the worker is next at the house. Mrs. Hile told us that she receives an average of about four calls per month from the housekeeper and about five per month from the residents. Since the housekeepers are highly experienced and well suited to their work, most of their calls involve genuine emergencies, as when a resident disappears, makes a suicide attempt, or presents some other major behavior problem. The calls from the residents are often not emergencies but rather result from anxiety about some development during the day or apprehension about some step that lies just ahead.

The energy, involvement, dedication, and practical knowledge of the social workers were impressive. From their description of their responsibilities and the way they meet them, they seemed to function at a very high level, with a competence that would do credit to more highly trained individuals. In addition to their responsibilities to present residents, Mrs. Hile provides ongoing counseling to ten former residents and Mr. Schlabach to five.

The housekeepers for each of the two houses are on duty during the unusual hours of 8 p.m. to noon of the following day (including, of course, the time that they are sleeping). The assistant housekeepers come in at 11 a.m. and work until 8 p.m., during which time they prepare dinner. Each housekeeper and the assistant share the responsibilities of planning meals, shopping, and cleaning the common rooms and the bathrooms. During the evening hours the residents often come to the housekeeper to talk over practical problems and to get advice and support. A careful attempt is made to differentiate the kind of transactions that the housekeepers may appropriately engage in with residents without stepping over into areas that call for professional competence. This seemed to be no problem at all, since the housekeepers were self-confident, sensitive women with a great deal of comfort about the roles they were expected to play. They are deliberately not called "housemothers" because of a concern that this term would evoke a negative response from some residents who have had trouble with their parents; but even so they seem to exude the warmth of a good mother, serving a useful function as comforter, confidante, and reality tester. They make it clear to the residents that intimate information confided in them will be passed on to the professional staff. They also make it clear that residents must not discuss with them either their past illness or the illness of fellow residents.

The residents

The sources of residents for the two halfway houses have varied from time to time, but the characteristics in terms of history of illness have remained reasonably constant; that is, the substantial majority of those accepted have had a diagnosis of schizophrenia. This is not because such applicants are favored, since any category of the mentally ill is eligible except those with a primary diagnosis of alcoholism or narcotics addiction, but rather because schizophrenics appear to constitute the major category of those who seem to need the experience of living in a specialized transitional setting. Behavior, however, is considered more important than diagnosis; in interviewing candidates, the staff looks for *a*) willingness and capacity to live in a group, *b*) potential employability, and *c*) ability to assume a reasonable level of responsibility for oneself in such matters as maintaining a relationship with a therapist, taking one's medication, and so on. Ideally, some plan for training or employment will have been worked out by the referring agency, or by the halfway house social worker, before the applicant moves in. By and large the prospective resident must be sufficiently stabilized to be successfully carried on an outpatient basis. The only community mental health center serving Indianapolis to date operates a day hospital, and recently some day patients have been accepted at Gateways.

In the first dozen years of its existence, Gateways for Women had 158 different residents; the largest group, 30 percent, came from Central State Hospital, located about five miles away. The next largest group, 22 percent, came from Larue Carter Memorial Hospital, a small (200-bed) state hospital which is permitted to select patients in terms of their suitability for its training program. A total of 23 percent came from four state hospitals located at some distance from Indianapolis. Eleven percent came on referral from psychiatrists in private practice, and six percent from the psychiatric unit of the county general hospital. The remaining nine percent came from five other sources.

In its first two and a half years the men's house had 33 different residents. The modal group—52 percent—came from Larue Carter. This was largely attributable to the fact that for a time the house had only a part-time social worker, whose full-time employment was at Larue Carter, thus furnishing a built-in flow of referrals. The next largest group, 27 percent, came from Central State Hospital. The remaining 21 percent were spread among five other referral sources.

Both houses impose a lower age limit of 17, but no upper age limit. The men have averaged 26 years of age and thus have been younger than the women, who have averaged 34 years. Eighteen percent of the men and ten percent of the women have been under 20; 64 percent of the men and 33 percent of the women have been between 20 and 30. Fifty-seven percent of the women but only 18 percent of the men have been over 30. A part of the age discrepancy is accounted for by the large number of men referred from Larue Carter, which tends to select for admission people who are undergoing their first psychiatric hospitalization and are therefore younger than the population of most state hospitals.

Compared to some of the other houses that we visited, there seems to have been a fair amount of acting-out behavior, for reasons that are not altogether clear. There have been various suicide gestures and attempts at the women's house, and in the few months prior to our visit it had been necessary for two of the women to be taken to the hospital for lavage and in another case for the police to assist in disarming a young woman who was wielding a butcher knife after having taken an overdose of medication. There have also been several fights among residents, but in each case the staff has been able to restore peace without having to ask anyone to leave.

Negroes are underrepresented among the residents. This is not because of policy, but simply because there have been scarcely any Negro referrals to the program; every Negro referred has been accepted.

The program

The stated goals and objectives of the halfway houses are to provide

> homelike living arrangements, and at the same time [give] the resident support in a benign atmosphere, [affording] a period of transition during which the patient regains a measure of self-reliance and economic independence. The halfway house gives the resident a chance to "test his wings" and at the same time "get his feet off the ground."

An important advantage of the halfway house is seen as its providing a place where the former patient does not have to live under the pressure of hiding his recent hospitalization from the people that he is living with. Even if the only common denominator in the house is the fact of previous psychiatric care, this "eases the anxiety of dealing with the many stigmas that face the returning patient."

The house is seen as providing many rehabilitative experiences: it gives the resident a supportive base from which to learn his way about the city; an opportunity to measure himself again against society's standards for good grooming and personal hygiene; a chance to redevelop the responsibility for maintaining himself on the job; experiences in choosing his own clothing, doing his own budgeting, seeking his own entertainment, affiliating with a church, and establishing friendships. And the house provides "an address from which to apply for a job, [since] the stigma against employing ex-mental patients is still great, and many employers may not grant appointments to applicants from mental hospitals."

Thus, the purpose of the program is to provide opportunities and assistance in a variety of ways to help the resident re-establish (or establish) independent living patterns and effective relationships. It is not, in the more restricted meaning of the term, a treatment program. There is little feel of a clinically oriented mental health facility; there are no formal therapy sessions, no psychiatric confrontations, nor a psychiatric consultant on the paid staff. The prevailing flavor is close to that of a supportive boardinghouse, with strong emphasis on a homelike, almost dormitory type of climate. The underlying philosophy might be characterized as "reality therapy," at the other end of the spectrum from the psychoanalytic approach.

Prospective residents must be referred by a psychiatric hospital, the psychiatric service of a general hospital, a psychiatric clinic, or a psychiatrist in private practice. They need not be residents of Marion County (Indianapolis), but in the event of a demand for space that outruns the supply (this has rarely happened), preference would be given to the resident of the county. The applicant must be old enough to accept employment, and he must have a plan formulated whereby he will be working, on job training, or in school. His medical requirements must be arranged by the referral source and must be provided by an Indianapolis facility. It must be determined that he will need a period of group living before he will be able to move on to a more autonomous living arrangement in the community. And his prognosis must indicate a strong likelihood that he will be able, following the group-living experience, to move on to a more independent type of living in the community. Although there is no formal limit on stay, "the intent of the halfway house is to provide a transitional residence rather than a long-term sheltered living arrangement."

The intake procedure at these two halfway houses is perhaps the most intricate among the eleven programs we visited. It usually begins with a telephone call to the social worker. Many of the calls concern inquiries which do not materialize, sometimes because of gross inappropriateness, and consequently about half of the would-be residents are screened out in the course of the initial call. For each who seems to meet the eligibility criteria, the referring source is asked to send a complete medical/psychiatric/social summary, setting forth the length of hospitalization, diagnosis, treatment, and a report of the patient's current mental status from his psychiatrist. The applicant's present adjustment, financial situation, and vocational plans and potentials must also be described. In addition, the agency must complete a one-page referral form provided by the mental health association. The development and transmittal of all this information is likely to require several days at minimum; the social workers often find that when it is submitted some important parts are missing, thus requiring additional time while the application is made complete.

When the information is all in hand, an interview of about two hours is scheduled at the social worker's office in the mental health association, following which the applicant, accompanied by the social worker, visits the house.

A summary of the interview, along with the case record, is sent to one of five psychiatrists who make up a professional advisory committee. The psychiatrist reviews the material and the social worker's recommendation for acceptance or rejection along with the treatment plan.

Of those who survive the initial telephone call, almost half do not move any further, for a variety of reasons, a principal one being some change in condition during the interval in which the required information is being assembled. Quite frequently this change in condition is the patient's unwillingness to accept a posthospital group-living situation.

In 1969, 31 formal applications were received for the women's house, of which eleven were withdrawn by the referral source, three were rejected, and seventeen were admitted. Of the twenty applications completed, the social worker's opinion was confirmed in every case by the members of the professional advisory committee. One of the three rejected was a woman with an obsessive-compulsive ritual so elaborate that it prevented her from going to bed at night; the other was a teenager who seemed to have essentially no ability to control her actions and behavior and thus seemed unlikely to be able to handle the considerable freedom of movement that characterizes Gateways; the third applicant's prognosis indicated a need for long-term sheltered living and employment.

We pursued with the staff whether all of the information requested was in fact essential, and whether the screening by a member of the professional advisory committee—particularly since its members had never reversed the recommendation of the social workers—was really useful, or whether it was to some extent a holdover from earlier days when the halfway house was a more daring and unorthodox notion than it has since come to be. The extensive data required were felt to be useful because they give the social worker a richer picture of the residents' previous experiences, both successful and unsuccessful, a description of their methods of coping with stress, family members' attitude, acceptance, willingness, and ability to help or hinder their independent adjustment to community living, the factors precipitating hospitalization, the effects of various treatment methods, the current and continuing treatment plan of the referral source including medication, and, in all, to know the residents' strengths and weaknesses in order to make the halfway house more meaningful than a simple boarding home experience.

It is not uncommon for the residents at Gateways to have had any-where from six to twelve years of continuous hospitalization, with little or no off-hospital-grounds experience. Accepting such residents without full data seems to the social worker at the women's house to be "like buying a can without a label."

The screening by the professional advisory committee was felt to be important largely in the case of applicants being turned down. Said Mr. Skole, "We don't want to be in the position of telling psychiatrists that they don't know their patients well enough to judge which will do well in our kind of setting, and consequently the review by a member of the professional advisory committee lends credence to and supports the social worker's recommendation."

Under optimum conditions the entire procedure can be completed in about two weeks, but in other cases may stretch to several weeks longer. More recently a new intake procedure has been established that stream-lines the process. Because the new Marion County General Hospital Community Mental Health Center has an average inpatient stay of only nineteen days, it needed its candidates to be processed more rapidly. Arrangements were thus worked out to accept the applicant on one day's notice, with the proviso that the community mental health center would provide ongoing psychiatric supervision and would in any needed case readmit the person immediately from the halfway house to its own inpatient service. At the time of our visit too few residents had been admitted under this new procedure to be able to judge how well it would work out, or to determine whether the outcome with this process was significantly different from that under the traditional intake pattern.

T HERE ARE DELIBERATELY FEW PROGRAMMED ACTIVITIES within the houses, since "we encourage the residents to participate in the ordinary social milieu of the community in whatever ways they find enjoyable and fruitful." Some residents move into community activities fairly easily, often through church membership and the people with whom they work. Others find it more difficult, and for this reason the alumnae association of a college sorority has established a weekly social program at the women's house. These are sometimes outside events, such as plays and concerts, swimming parties, and bowling, or something as simple as a shopping trip to the drugstore; sometimes they are events at the house, such as card parties and films. About a dozen women volunteers participate regularly in these activities. Such a group has not been recruited to provide activities at the men's house, but the social worker accompanies the men each week to some outside event such as bowling, basketball games, and miniature golf. More recently there have been occasional parties between the two houses, particularly at holidays.

Residents are given certain responsibilities, such as carrying their own door keys, signing out when they will return late or stay away overnight, and managing their own medication. (Only in the case of a suicide risk does the housekeeper hold the medication, and then usually only for a few days.) They are not expected to do the major house cleaning, but are expected to clean and keep their own room in order, do their personal laundry, prepare their own meal if present at noon, set up and clear the table at dinner time, help tidy the common rooms, and, particularly when out of work, to sweep porches and walks, carry out trash, clean bathrooms, and generally assist the housekeepers. In addition the residents are encouraged to take opportunities to help prepare meals and make special dishes for all the residents.

A T LEAST IN THE CASE OF THE WOMEN'S HOUSE, the setting is so attractive that one might wonder what factors motivate the residents to leave. From our interviews both with staff and residents, the following factors emerged:

1. It is the value and stated goal to establish independent living.

2. The program deliberately does not give the resident any more than seems essential. As one resident put it, time weighs heavily if one does not exert himself and obtain work; hanging around the house can be boring.

3. Despite their having all undergone psychiatric treatment, many of the residents do not otherwise find much in common that binds them as a group.

4. The absence of formal therapeutic activities such as group therapy may serve to reduce dependency and encourage the resident to leave.

T HE NATURE OF THE RECORDS maintained on residents deserves comment. There is a case record for each person, and those that we examined were considerably more complete and of better quality than most that we have seen in formal treatment facilities. The record contains complete information furnished by the referring source, correspondence, information about finances, face-sheet data with identifying information, the preadmission evaluation made prior to the decision for admission, social worker entries describing the resident's adjustment during his stay at the house, monthly progress notes to the referring agency, information about current medication, and a list of the numerous contacts made with agencies on the resident's behalf. Each concludes with a discharge note as of the time the resident left the halfway house.

These records are of decidedly superior quality. Whether the time they require is necessary to most halfway houses seems open to inquiry.

Medication and medical service

Each resident is required to be under the care of a physician, who in substantially all cases is a psychiatrist. Those residents referred from an Indianapolis facility typically continue under its care. When a resident is referred from out of town, arrangements are made for local psychiatric follow-up to be provided, usually by the Marion County General Hospital Community Mental Health Center.

The frequency and nature of follow-up service is cooperatively determined with the treating facility. The halfway house staff maintain contact with it and participate in the formulation and review of the therapeutic plan and suggest the need for special attention if a resident seems to be having difficulty.

Substantially all of the residents—from eighty to ninety percent—take psychoactive medications. As we have said, each is responsible for maintaining and taking his own, although the housekeeper will occasionally take responsibility for a few days in specifically indicated cases. If the resident comes from either of the state hospitals in Indianapolis, he obtains medication there without charge. Some of the state hospitals outside of Indianapolis will mail medication to the patients they have referred, on request from the physician providing local follow-up. Patients of the mental health center obtain their medication at the pharmacy there at cost based on ability to pay. An occasional patient who has the means to pay for medication obtains it from some private pharmacy.

Medication is viewed as extremely important. Mr. Skole regards negligence in taking medication, along with problems about adjusting to employment, as the two principal reasons why residents have to return to hospital.

Physical illnesses are handled by the institution or clinic which is doing the follow-up. Some residents may have their own private family doctor or general practitioner; some are able to receive medical attention for physical illness by the staff physician in some of the sheltered workshops.

Outcome

The average length of stay for all of the women who had resided at Gateways through the end of 1969 was seven months; for the men, six and a half months. About 56 percent of the men stayed at the house between one and six months, and about 57 percent of the women stayed between one and nine months.

Just as there are no hard and fast limits on stay, neither is there a formal process for termination. Several factors, such as the individual's work or school progress, his seeming readiness to live more autonomously, and his financial resources, are reviewed by the halfway house social worker in collaboration with staff from the referral source, and a plan is formulated.

Like most other transitional residence programs, this one has incomplete information about what happens to residents once they have left the program. However, at the time of our visit it was in process of completing one of the more ambitious follow-up studies that we know of. Outcome data had been compiled for the first 114 women who had lived at Gateways, measuring such variables as employment status and number and duration of subsequent hospitalizations. The information had been encoded on IBM cards and was being analyzed.

During the year prior to our visit, a total of 28 residents had left the two halfway houses. Seven of these, or 25 percent, returned directly to the hospital; 18, or 64 percent, moved to autonomous living arrangements; and the other three either could not be located or returned to live with families. The rehospitalization rate of 25 percent compares with a rehospitalization rate of 32 percent for all patients released from the state hospitals in Indiana.

Agency and community relationships

Perhaps the most consequential of the program's relationships are those with the referring agencies. Neither of the halfway houses operates at capacity very much of the time. This seems an unlikely situation, considering the number of patients being discharged to the Indianapolis area and the relatively small capacity of the two houses. It results from the failure of the hospitals to refer more, and more appropriate, prospective residents. Their failure to do so seems to be related to two factors: a) not being sufficiently well informed about the program, they make few referrals, and b) they are unwilling to accept the application process and/or hesitate to compile the application information which the program requires. We have described the new arrangement with the community mental health center which significantly shortens the intake period; should this work out well, it may be that the intake procedure for all applicants will be simplified.

A psychiatrist from the men's service at Larue Carter Memorial Hospital told us that during the several months prior to our visit she had made no referrals to the men's halfway house. This was not because her patients did not need specialized living arrangements following discharge, but rather because most of them were young and it had been possible in most cases to arrange for several to move out together to share a house or apartment.

The state department of mental health seems highly supportive of the halfway houses. Since 1967 it has provided some financial support. In doing so it set forth certain requirements, all of which the program was already meeting; principal among these were that residents would have to be accepted regardless of ability to pay and regardless of referral source and that 24-hour staff coverage must be provided.

As we have indicated, most applicants are expected to be able to work or, at minimum, to be in a training program. The approximately forty percent in training programs are for the most part sponsored by the Division of Vocational Rehabilitation, which has readily provided sponsorship. Residents are accepted even though they need a sheltered workshop but hopefully can progress to the point of being able to live autonomously. Both Goodwill Industries and Crossroads (the local branch of the Society for Crippled Children and Adults) have readily accepted the residents for sheltered workshop and/or training programs.

The state employment service has frequently helped to line up employment for residents, including those who have failed in the initial job plan and need a new placement.

There were some initial complaints from neighbors about the advent of halfway houses in their neighborhoods. These were dealt with as they arose and for some time there have been essentially no complaints. At the same time, the relationships with neighbors are quite limited.

Financing

The two houses combined operate on a budget of about $70,000 per year. The principal source of income is the block grant provided by the state department of mental health, accounting for about 50 percent. Next come payments for room and board for the residents, accounting for about thirty percent. Some of this represents funds provided for individual patients from state hospitals on a fee-for-service basis, but the majority represents money paid in from the earnings of residents who are working. The balance of the income, about twenty percent, is provided by the United Fund of Greater Indianapolis.

The principal expenditures are salaries and benefits (68 percent) and food and household supplies (19 percent).

The costs of operating the houses would of course be higher if the rentals—$100 per month for the men's house, $1 per year for the women's house—were not so reasonable. As it is, the cost per resident figures out to about $10.50 per day including all services. This compares with a per diem cost for Indiana state hospitals, state-wide, of $12, and a per diem cost of about $55.50 for Larue Carter in particular.

XIII. McKinney House for Men
New Orleans Halfway House for Women
New Orleans

M CKINNEY HOUSE, A HALFWAY HOUSE FOR MEN, was established in
1964 at the instigation of the Louisiana Association for Mental
Health.[1] The association's interest in rehabilitation of people who have
been patients in state mental hospitals is long-standing. In 1959, under
the direction of one of the consultants engaged in this study (Mabel
Palmer), the association established the Magnolia Club, a social club
for former state hospital patients. It meets weekly at the association's
building, where it provides a program limited chiefly to opportunities
to socialize.

"With time," Miss Palmer told us, "the members came to visit us
more and more in between the scheduled meetings of the club. It became evident that many of them were having trouble staying out of the
hospital, frequently because they could not find a supportive kind of
place to live. They were living in unsatisfactory boardinghouses and
suffering from a lack of the environmental supports they needed."

Consequently, she approached the state's Division of Vocational Rehabilitation to discuss the possibility of creating a halfway house. From
an initial survey, it appeared that among the one thousand people a year
returning to the New Orleans area from state hospitals, there might be
one third or more who could benefit from the specialized living experience that a halfway house provides. The majority of this group were
men.

With encouragement from the vocational rehabilitation officials, the
mental health association proceeded to submit an application to the
federal vocational rehabilitation agency for a demonstration grant that
would provide the funds to establish a halfway house for men. A one-

---

[1] Located in New Orleans, the Louisiana association differs from most others in that
the state organization also provides a local program, "simply because so much of
our money and leadership comes from this area that if we had a separate local
program it would drain off so much of our resources that the state organization
would suffer."

129

year grant, renewable for two additional years, was awarded effective in late 1964, intended to demonstrate whether a halfway house would reduce the readmission rate to state hospitals.

Then came the search for a suitable location. Large houses are greatly in demand in New Orleans, and expensive. Eventually Miss Palmer located a big and rather dilapidated former private residence that had been used by a general hospital to house its medical library. "With a great deal of begging and borrowing," the association recruited the funds to get the house into habitable condition, and the first residents moved in in July 1965.

At the outset the mental health association had decided that it would limit its direct involvement to the three-year period of the demonstration grant, since it could not permanently afford to siphon off the time and effort from its educational and legislative responsibilities. During that early period Miss Palmer devoted almost half of her time to McKinney House affairs, while from the outset she sought to identify a sponsorship that would take over following the demonstration period. The state Division of Vocational Rehabilitation subsequently agreed that it would become the permanent sponsor of McKinney House, provided a small amount of local funds could be raised.

The mental health association thereupon prevailed on the city government to earmark $5000 per year to be given to the association, which would in turn remit the funds to the state rehabilitation agency. Thus, since the expiration of the federal grant in October 1967, McKinney House has operated as a state-sponsored facility. Late in 1969 a second house was opened for women. A little earlier, in mid-1968, a house for men had been established in Baton Rouge (as a result of efforts of the local mental health association). Thus, at the time of our visit in early 1970, the state agency was operating three halfway houses for former mental patients—the McKinney House for Men, the New Orleans Halfway House for Women, and the Baton Rouge Halfway House for Men.

Physical facilities

For several years McKinney House remained at its original premises, but with each passing year the building showed more signs of aging and called for ever more extensive repairs. Eventually the renovation demands became overwhelming, and a search was undertaken for a new location. In March 1970 the program moved to a large and attractive two-story white frame house, located on a corner in a solidly middle-class residential section, within two blocks of a main artery and public transportation and near Tulane University. The program was still getting settled in its new quarters at the time of our visit. The interior of the house is newly refinished and is particularly bright and cheerful. The first floor consists of a spacious living room, a dining room, and a kitchen, plus two offices for the staff. The second floor contains bedrooms, each accommodating two or three men, with a total capacity of thirteen. Everything was remarkably clean.

The Halfway House for Women is located several miles away. Almost everything we have said of the men's house can also be said of the women's house. It, too, is in a solidly middle-class neighborhood. It is a large, pleasant, two-story frame house, with a good-sized living room, a dining room, and a kitchen. The eleven women residents have their bedrooms on the second floor. The house is a short walk from public transportation. All in all, it is less modern than the men's house and at the same time more homelike, with personal effects more in evidence.

Both of the houses are rented.

When the original McKinney House was in the planning stages, the mental health association decided to wage an educational campaign to the surrounding community. However much effect this campaign may have had, in any case the original McKinney House, in a rather more anonymous neighborhood than at present, had no trouble with its neighbors. When the new McKinney House was located, it was decided not to attempt to prepare the neighborhood for its advent. Some of the neighbors became quite threatened by the establishment of a facility to serve people with a history of mental illness. They were concerned that their children would be harmed and that their property values would go down. A few came in person to McKinney House to protest; the staff has done its utmost to reassure them but has not been cowed, since the program legally occupies its premises in conformity with zoning and occupancy regulations. After taking occupancy, the staff arranged an open house to which the neighbors were invited. Only three persons, all of them hostile to the program, attended.

An intensive educational effort with the neighbors was undertaken for the women's house and thus far it has had no problems.

The staff and the board believe there would be many advantages to having the men's and women's houses located side by side rather than many miles apart. Such an arrangement would reduce travel time for the staff, allow more efficient and economical food ordering, and provide convenient social opportunities. However, there does not seem to be any interest in mixing men and women within the same house; this reluctance seems to stem mainly from the concern that this would be unacceptable to the public officials involved with the house and to the surrounding community.

The staff

All of the staff are state employees of the Division of Vocational Rehabilitation. A vocational counselor who has a master's degree in social work, Fred Memleb, carries out administrative and supervisory functions for both houses. This encompasses all dealings with the state Division of Vocational Rehabilitation, including an enormous amount of paper work required for each resident, plus the negotiation of a maze of regulations about purchasing, maintenance, repairs, and so on that are altogether unknown to some of the independent halfway houses we visited. Mr. Memleb also participates in the initial screening of candidates for the two houses. He runs a weekly counseling group at each house, and in addition acts as counselor to a number of former residents who have moved on from the halfway houses. He works with residents individually when this seems indicated. He also is on call for nighttime and weekend coverage and backup of the live-in staff. He spends one day per week at the Southeastern Mental Health Clinic in order to broaden his own skills and understanding of mental illness. Mr. Memleb puts in long hours for modest pay. He seems to be cognizant of the needs of the residents and to take a great interest in and show a great concern for their well-being. He is assisted by a secretary.

McKinney House has a housemother, a cook, and a live-in student. The student, in the graduate school of social work at Louisiana State University, is on duty evenings and weekends and at other times when the housemother is off duty. He does the cooking on Sundays. He receives free room and board but no salary (although there are plans for a moderate salary in the future).

The Halfway House for Women has houseparents and a cook. The houseparents are an older couple without previous experience in working with the mentally ill. The woman is a full-time employee; her husband is retired and works only occasionally, taking care of the maintenance of the house. We found the housemother particularly interesting. Initially reluctant to take the job because of her lack of experience, she seemed to have come to be highly pleased with it. Having raised seven children of her own as well as a number of foster children, she takes a motherly interest in "her girls." She provides a sympathetic ear, giving particular support at the time a resident first begins work. She and her husband seemed to be sensitive, warm, empathic people who were intrigued by the problems of the mentally ill but at the same time focused on the strengths and capabilities of the residents.

The program has two psychiatric consultants. One, Dr. Thomas Rafferty, has been involved since the earliest days, and was for some time a half-time member of the staff. These men attend the weekly staff meetings and are otherwise available on call for emergencies and special problems (which rarely occur). It seemed evident that both of them carry considerable weight both with the vocational counselor who heads up the program and with the state Division of Vocational Rehabilitation.

The residents

During fiscal 1969, 45 men lived at McKinney House. They ranged in age from 17 to 61, with an average age of 25; well over half were in their twenties. They showed a quite high average educational level (12.2 years); there was one Ph.D. candidate, nine with some college training, and most of the rest had completed high school.

The average number of hospitalizations was 2.5, with a range from zero to 7. The average length of hospitalization was 11.1 months, with a range from zero to 28 months.

The women's house was too new for there to have been enough residents for a summary of their characteristics to be useful.

The program

Both the state hospitals and the community resources that refer candidates to the halfway houses seem to be well acquainted with the program and its purposes. The referring agency is asked to submit a history of the candidate, and an appointment is arranged with Mr. Memleb, who explains the goals of the houses and what is expected of the residents. The candidate and Mr. Memleb attempt to develop a suitable vocational plan. This in turn is presented to a weekly staff meeting which is attended by Mr. Memleb, the two psychiatric consultants, a representative of the mental health association, a senior counselor from the local office of the state Division of Vocational Rehabilitation, the housemothers of the two houses, and the student who lives at McKinney House. The candidate is presented to this group, which discusses his proposed program with him. Almost all of the persons who survive the intake process to the point of coming before the staff meeting are accepted; only two had been turned down in the six months prior to our visit. Certain types of persons are generally excluded, particularly those alcoholics who do not seem to be able to refrain from drinking, and homosexuals who it is thought might be sexually active within the house. Each resident is advised that no drinking is permitted in the house and that physically abusive behavior is not tolerated. The intake process can involve as little as a week, rarely requires more than a month, but in unusual cases can run to several months.

There is no formal limit on how long a resident may stay. In actuality, the average length of stay is between four and five months for the men. Since each resident enters the program with vocational goals already formulated, the outcome hoped for is that the resident will complete his vocational preparation, start work, remain in the house for about six weeks while he becomes stabilized in his new job, then move on to a more autonomous living arrangement. The residents who move on to apartments and boardinghouses usually continue to see Mr. Memleb for brief counseling for a period of two or three months, occasionally longer.

There are no formal age limits, but, since vocational placement is the program's foremost goal, rarely is anyone under 16 or over 60 accepted. Most of the residents are between 20 and 35, and it is this age bracket with which the houses seem to feel most comfortable and achieve the best results.

At neither house is there a scheduled program of evening activities. The residents come home about five o'clock, have their evening meal a short time afterward, then either retire to their rooms, watch television, play Ping-pong or card games, or go outside the house for entertainment. "Quiet hours" are in effect from ten o'clock onward; however, there is no curfew. As Miss Palmer put it, "We would rather have a resident coming in at midnight than struggle to keep him out of bed until 9 p.m."

We were provided an awesome list of rules that had been developed some time earlier for the men's house. However, as it turned out, a good many of the rules may need never have been formulated, since there were no problems of violation or enforcement. Consequently the list did not seem to carry much weight, and the residents themselves were in process of developing a less restrictive and more realistic set of rules for themselves.

More than most of the other halfway houses that we visited, these mandate participation in a psychiatric treatment program. All of the residents are required to attend weekly group therapy sessions led by the other of the two psychiatric consultants, Dr. W. L. Walls, at the Southeastern Clinic in downtown New Orleans. This state-supported clinic agreed, in the planning stage for the program, that it would provide the psychiatric services needed by the residents. There are two sexually mixed groups; that is, residents of the men's and women's houses are divided into two groups of approximately equal size and intermixed. Dr. Walls prefers the group technique not simply because it is more economical of time but because he feels that the halfway house caseload, with its heavy representation of schizophrenics and alcoholics, is best served by the interpersonal transactions that group treatment fosters. The groups were described to us as rather confronting in nature; this did not seem to be a source of distress to any of the residents that we interviewed.

The women fix their own breakfast and lunch and clean up afterward. The housemothers plan the menus and do the shopping. As we have mentioned, each house has a cook. While this arrangement may make for a more orderly situation than having the residents do all the cooking, on the other hand it reduces the opportunity to acquire or enhance their skills in an everyday competence that will be required of them when they leave the halfway houses to take up autonomous living arrangements in the community.

Special occasions such as holidays are celebrated jointly—sometimes in one house, sometimes the other. The women's house more commonly observes birthdays, sometimes with assistance from a civic group.

Medication and medical service

Substantially all of the residents take psychotropic drugs and, in the case of the alcoholics, Antabuse. Medications are prescribed for almost all of the patients by Dr. Walls at the Southeastern Clinic. He prefers to keep the medication transaction entirely separate from the group therapy sessions, and consequently he sees the residents to review their medication usually at monthly intervals, or more frequently when indicated in a particular case. The residents are responsible for keeping and taking their own medications. The housemother at the women's house told us, however, that she supervises the Antabuse medication each morning for the alcoholic residents.

In the early years of McKinney House, when it was located opposite the Touro Infirmary, the men simply walked across the street to see the doctor when they had any physical health problems.

By design, none of the therapists involved with the residents ever come to see them at the halfway houses, except in the very rare case of an emergency. This practice stems from an awareness that the residents will be unlikely to receive home visits after they move away from the halfway house, and thus they are habituated to going to the professional.

Outcome

The latest figures available for McKinney House (fiscal 1969) indicate that it has a remarkably successful outcome by the criteria of moving on to autonomous living conditions and to a job. Of 45 men who lived in the house, only four (nine percent) were rehospitalized. Five (11 percent) transferred or "graduated" to other rehabilitation plans, while 36 (80 percent) succeeded in becoming employed and moving to more independent quarters.

Agency and community relationships

McKinney House and the Halfway House for Women are part and parcel of the state vocational rehabilitation program. Consequently it is not to the point to characterize the state program as "an agency to which the houses relate." However, because the impetus for the houses arose locally and because there is important local representation on the admissions committee, it is important to consider the quality of the "local vs. state" relationship. When McKinney House was still in the planning phase, the state vocational rehabilitation office encouraged the state mental health association to apply for federal demonstration funds, and it later agreed to take over the funding and operating of the house when the demonstration grant expired. Even so, it appears almost certain that without local initiative, and, at the present time, local support, the houses would fare less well. There have been frequent problems of getting state authorization for needed supplies and repair work. The amount of paper work and the numerous regulations greatly exceed that of most of the other programs we visited. On the other hand, we must keep in mind that the goal of this program is more complex and demanding than that of halfway houses which are content simply to help people stay out of the hospital; at McKinney House and the Halfway House for Women, the articulated goal is to get the person not only into some autonomous living arrangement but also into suitable employment.

The relationship with the treating facility, the Southeastern Clinic, appears to be an integral and highly successful one, providing reasonably convenient and quickly accessible service.

In New Orleans are several day hospitals that are almost always available for the occasional halfway house resident who temporarily needs the support of a day treatment program. There is also a private sheltered workshop available, but it is rarely used since the vocational goal for practically all of the halfway house residents is regular competitive employment. Mr. Memleb himself has developed a roster of about ten firms that will occasionally provide a job for one of the halfway house residents.

Financing

Except for $5000 per year provided by the City of New Orleans, the halfway houses are entirely funded by the Louisiana Division of Vocational Rehabilitation. A budget for the new Halfway House for Women was not available; the budget for McKinney House during fiscal 1969 was just under $32,000, a figure that includes room and board plus all of the supportive and counseling services provided within the house. This breaks down to $5.60 per resident per day, a very modest cost for the good quality of the services provided. The per diem expenditure at the state hospital during this same period was slightly over $20.

The Division of Vocational Rehabilitation also pays the tuition for each resident who is in a vocational training program. This varies from about $600 for a secretarial course up to about $1500 for a welding course.

As long as the resident is in training, Vocational Rehabilitation covers his expenses. Once he is placed in a job, he is expected, for the additional time that he remains in the halfway house, to pay as much as possible toward the $85 per month room-and-board charge. At the time of our visit several residents in each house were paying the full amount. These fees are credited to the general receipts of Vocational Rehabilitation, not to the halfway house budgets.

Not included in these figures are the psychotherapy and other medical services provided by the Southeastern Clinic.

Future plans

Both McKinney House and the Halfway House for Women were still settling in at the time of our visit, and at that time there was no talk of expansion. Almost all of the people we interviewed, however, expressed the view that numerous additional halfway houses are needed—additional ones for the general run of psychiatric patients, plus some specialized ones for narcotics addicts, alcoholics, young people, and old people. Also, longer-term community residences are needed for people who can live outside the hospital provided they have a structured and supportive living arrangement available. The state Division of Vocational Rehabilitation estimates that perhaps as many as 25 percent of all those living in the halfway houses it operates around the state are people who have a history of mental illness.

Even so, if the findings of the original survey carried out in conjunction with the planning for McKinney House are anywhere near correct—that is, that between three hundred and four hundred people being discharged to the New Orleans area from state hospitals each year could benefit from halfway house residence—then the existing program is indeed meeting only a tiny fraction of the need.

XIV. Gilead House
Middletown, Connecticut

G ILEAD HOUSE IS A RELATIVELY NEW HALFWAY HOUSE whose residents are a mixture of undergraduate students from Wesleyan University and former patients from Connecticut's state and private psychiatric hospitals. Situated in a residential area that is a short walk from the campus, it operates with professional endorsement and backup, but with no trained staff living in the house. It is one of only two halfway houses that we identified that involve college students.

Origins

In the short time since it was established in the fall of 1968, Gilead House has had several changes of residents and directors, and no historical account of its development has been kept. Consequently, tracing its history is a matter of relying on the recall of several of the persons who had been in one way or another involved with the house and were still on the scene at the time of our visit.

The experience that led to the idea of creating Gilead House is clear enough. The State of Connecticut each summer operates a ten-week "Service Corps," which involves about two hundred students from all over the country and from various foreign countries. They are assigned to the state's three mental hospitals and to various other mental health department activities. During the summer of 1968, about twenty students were assigned to work with a group of Connecticut Valley Hospital patients in building a summer camp. Among the students were two men from Wesleyan. In the course of their contacts with the patients, they observed that some did not seem to behave in ways that required them to be in a state hospital, and they were concerned that these patients would have to return to the hospital simply because there was no available place for them in the community.

They took their concern to Dr. Richard Wiseman, a psychologist who was at that time assistant director of psychological services for the state department of mental health, and also the supervisor of the summer

139

camp. He encouraged them and offered to provide such backup from the state department as could be arranged.

The students then returned to Middletown and presented their proposal to the university administration, which agreed to rent them a large nearby house. Concurrently, the students elicited the support of a group of local people, including mental health professionals, clergymen, prominent laymen, and university personnel, who became the board of directors. When Gilead House opened, it was designed to accommodate seven college students and eight former patients. In October 1968 the first students moved in, and shortly thereafter the patients began to be referred from the state hospital.

THE FIRST YEAR WAS FRAUGHT WITH PROBLEMS. None of the people involved had had any prior experience with a halfway house. Everything was carried out on a trial-and-error basis. There were few rules, no assignments of duties. One willing college student ended up doing all of the cooking. Because all of the participants were somewhat anxious and defensive about what the neighbors would think of them, no efforts were made to acquaint the people living around them with their purposes or goals. Before long a small menagerie had developed, with not only dogs and cats but also chickens and a sheep.

The initial referrals from the state hospital were older, long-hospitalized schizophrenics, of the kind that the Wesleyan students had been dealing with in the summer camp program. But in the confines of the house a decided age gap developed, with the young students and the older patients finding themselves essentially estranged from each other. The various problems were rather well concealed from the board of directors, the university, and the community. But at the end of its first year, Gilead House was less than the success its originators had hoped for. Of the patients referred there, two went back to the hospital, both on their own initiative; others remained at the house, with little effort on anyone's part to help them find jobs or move on to some autonomous type of living arrangement. Only one former patient left the house to live in the community.

In the summer of 1969, a psychology major named James Monahan came to Gilead House as its new director. He took over with a firm hand. Most of the animals went. A roster for cleaning and cooking was set up, with each resident contributing his share. Arrangements were made with the hospitals to refer younger patients who, it was believed, would have more in common with the college students. Some rules were formulated, the foremost being *a*) no sexual activities within the house and *b*) no use of illegal drugs in the house. Those requirements were made plain to prospective residents, both students and ex-patients, with the understanding that infringement would lead to expulsion.

"We had to replace an essentially hippie atmosphere with something more normative," Mr. Monahan told us. "Whether sexual behavior and drug use were part of the contemporary college scene was beside the point, because in order to be useful to the residents we needed to provide them role models based on the kind of behavior that would be expected of them when they moved on to other living arrangements in the community. In other words, despite the fact that we were using college students as staff and were located in a college community, it would not do to impose the college culture on Gilead House."

One further step was to reduce the emotional dependence of the residents on the director. Said Mr. Monahan:

> The people who had been in the state hospital came here expecting to be treated like patients, to have their problems listened to, to be "cured." After a while I got tired of staying up until three in the morning listening to the same complaints and problems over and over again. I began to feel that the problems were not so much problems as they were a means of keeping me out of bed. So at that point, I told them I would no longer be available in that sense—that there were psychiatrists, psychologists, and clinics on the outside where they could continue their notion of patienthood, but that they were going to be treated as people and not as patients within Gilead House.

Mr. Monahan departed as director in the fall, to be replaced by Richard Hammer, a psychology major who had also served in the summer Service Corps. At the time of our visit to Gilead House, in February 1970, Mr. Hammer appeared not only to have retained but to have solidified the improvements that Mr. Monahan initiated. The ratio of students to ex-patients had been changed to nine ex-patients and six students. The house was running at capacity. It was clean and orderly. The residents were cooperating in cleaning, cooking, and other household duties. There were no problems of sexual behavior or drug use. There was a strong emphasis on the transitional nature of Gilead House and the goal of enabling its ex-patient residents to move on to autonomous living arrangements. And some positive results were beginning to be seen.

Physical facilities

Gilead House is located on a main street in a large, old, three-story frame house owned by Wesleyan University. On the first floor are two average-sized living rooms, a dining room, a well-equipped kitchen, and a single bedroom for the director. The second floor has four double bedrooms and a study for the men, the third floor three double bedrooms for the women. Of particular interest and importance is the fact that rooms are shared by students and former patients.

The house is strikingly similar to a college fraternity or sorority. The rooms are filled with books, radios, stereo sets, stuffed dolls, athletic equipment, and photographs of boy friends and girl friends.

The close proximity to the university is important, in that it allows the students to get to and from classes conveniently and to participate with ease in various aspects of campus life.

The staff

All of the residents of Gilead House who are not former mental patients are considered to be "staff." The only salaried position is that of the director, who in some cases has been a student concurrently, in other cases not. (Mr. Hammer, the director at the time of our visit, had received his bachelor's degree in psychology the previous summer and was taking a year's leave from school before pursuing his graduate work.) A second resident is designated the codirector, in exchange for which she receives free room and board.

Whether a student applying to live in the house is to be accepted is decided by the students already there. We talked with all who were living there at the time of our visit. They were all religion or psychology majors. They had heard about Gilead House either from friends who were previously acquainted with it, or from notices on bulletin boards and in the school newspaper. Unanimously they were pleased with the experience. Several of them said, however, that their grades had suffered because of the time-consuming obligations that their roles at Gilead House placed on them. They all felt that the period of residence in the house should be strictly limited for the students, perhaps to a single semester and in no case more than a year.

All of them said they had been apprehensive about coming to Gilead House, but that they would do it over again. It was significant that no student had ever moved out without completing his agreed-upon period of residence. The students said they did not believe that living in Gilead House was viewed by other Wesleyan students as "far out" on the one hand, or that it merited any special status on the other. Many of the Wesleyan students did not seem to know of the existence of Gilead House, and to those who did, to live there was considered to be a good thing to do, in that it demonstrated a commitment to the value of contributing one's time and capabilities to an activity that seemed relevant.

While the students seemed to be quite sensitive to the needs of the patient group, sometimes taking deliberate measures to try to increase self-esteem, they nonetheless expressed some concern that the former patients sometimes felt like "second-class citizens." The students were also aware that they should not "reinstitutionalize" residents at Gilead House, and thus they felt that the house should pursue a policy of firmness in terminating the ex-patient residents as soon as alternate living arrangements could be made for them.

These students impressed us as bright, dedicated, aware of their responsibilities, and probably very good role models for the resident group. They have allowed themselves the opportunity to learn how to deal with emotionally troubled people and to develop rules and approaches based primarily on their own life experiences. Even though several were psychology majors, what came through was their creative use of nonprofessional approaches to former patients.

Despite the favorable impression of Gilead House at the time of our visit, we could not help feeling that for the future it would benefit from a less rapid turnover of directors. Mr. Hammer was in process of leaving; fortunately, his successor was to be the assistant director who had a year's previous experience at Gilead and was therefore well acquainted with the demands of the job. The students may well be right about limiting the student experience to a semester or at most a year, but it probably would be beneficial to Gilead House if each director were to stay for at least a year.

There did not seem to be any specific requirements for the position of director, other than available time and approval by Dr. Wiseman and the board of directors. Undoubtedly, however, a great many attributes and skills are sought, including self-confidence, the ability to assume authority when necessary, reasonable articulateness, good perception of the needs of the mentally ill, and personal warmth. These characteristics seemed evident to us in the former director, the present director, and the future director.

Probably one of the most desirable benefits of the Gilead House experience for the students is a broadened perspective of what constitutes deviant behavior. We can safely assume that the students we interviewed are above average in tolerance; but even so it is a significant insight for a student to say, "Many of these ex-patients would not have been in the hospital if they had been enrolled at the university." The broadening influence on the students is another reason for limiting their period of residence, in the interest of involving a larger number of young people in this opportunity for growth.

Dr. Wiseman, the clinical director, comes once a week to Gilead House for a session with the students. This is a voluntary activity for which he receives no pay. He was characterized as nondirective and exploratory. All of the students that we talked with considered him to be extremely helpful. He is available to handle emergencies, but it has rarely been necessary to ask him to do so.

The residents

During 1969, fifteen different ex-patients lived at Gilead House. Eight were men, seven were women, and all of them were single. Seven each were under 21 and between 21 and 30, and only one was over 30 years old. While Gilead House in the recent past has indicated its availability as an alternative to admission to the state hospital, at the time of our visit only two residents had come to them other than from hospitals. Of these exceptions, one was referred by a vocational rehabilitation counselor, the other by a psychiatrist in private practice.

Most of the ex-patients must work in order to have money to pay Gilead House and for personal expenses. Although some could qualify for funds from welfare under the "Aid to the Disabled" category, Gilead House discourages this, on the grounds that the resident is unlikely to exert an effort as long as the welfare money is coming to him.

In one case, an unemployed resident thought by the staff to be able to work was given a choice of finding a job or moving out. He found a job.

In our efforts to learn something of the severity of the problems of the residents, we pursued with Mr. Hammer the question of the diagnoses that they had had in the hospital, but he protested that this is a matter largely outside the concern of Gilead House. "Whether these people have been psychotic in the past or not does not matter so much as the fact that they aren't acting psychotic when they come to us; consequently, we don't treat them as if they are sick." Furthermore, he added, the staff do not have professional credentials in the mental health professions and, therefore, should not be dealing with diagnoses. Finally, he felt that such knowledge often negatively alters the expectation one makes of the former patient, and cited examples of this from his experience working within the state hospital.

Ralph Mateo, coordinator of community services at Connecticut Valley Hospital, a newly appointed board member and the person designated as liaison agent between the hospital and Gilead House, told us that almost all of the ex-patients had in fact been diagnosed as schizophrenic. However, the majority of these quite young ex-patients had been hospitalized only briefly, and Mr. Mateo felt that a number of them would not have required hospitalization at all if they could have been sent to some appropriate alternate setting such as Gilead House.

Initially Gilead House decided not to admit young people with drug problems, but eventually decided to change this policy. At the time of our visit there were two men residents who had been in hospital because of their use of drugs. The house has maintained a policy of not accepting alcoholics (although alcoholics in the Gilead House age range—18 to 25—are almost nonexistent).

Both Dr. Wiseman and Mr. Hammer were inclined to see the problems of the residents more as social than medical. These young people may well need, however, a special type of resocialization (or initial socialization) that can be available only in a specialized facility such as Gilead House. Mr. Mateo stated that the patients who benefited most from Gilead House were those who needed a youth-oriented culture and peer-group support and were unable to find these on their own.

The program

The Gilead House program might be best described as a patterned "experience in living." In almost all respects the students and the ex-patients are peers, an exception being the weekly meeting of the students and the clinical consultant, from which the ex-patients are usually excluded.

When we asked whether Gilead House had a patient government, Mr. Hammer replied that it does not because "we do not recognize the status of 'patient' within the house." Instead, there are weekly meetings of all the residents, run by the director and concerning problems of personal interactions and of the responsibilities around the house. However, the house is in the process of permitting each member to run these house meetings. Such a role enables the group to explore each individual's potential for leadership.

All residents are expected to take care of their own rooms. They may elect to keep them as tidy or as messy as they choose, provided that they do not go so far as to create a fire or health hazard. At the time of our visit, all the rooms seemed at least as neat and tidy as most college dormitories and fraternities that we have seen.

As for the cleaning, cooking, and maintenance of the common areas, there is a duty roster covering each such activity. There is, for example, a garbage detail involving two residents for a one-week period. The residents prepare their own breakfasts and lunches, but each must take his turn in preparing dinner. The director does the grocery shopping, usually accompanied by one or two of the residents. Each person may decide what he wants to cook from the supplies that are on hand; if there are too many easy outs, such as frankfurters and beans, group pressure usually results in an improvement. There are special "clean-up drives" from time to time.

Lectures, movies, concerts, and similar events at Wesleyan University are available to the ex-patient residents without charge. Often members of the house attend these functions together. There are also special social activities such as picnics and holiday dinners that are individually developed. But there are no regularly scheduled social activities. The staff members feel that "any pre-established activities inhibit the function of our total membership as a group." Mr. Hammer expressed the view that if the staff regularly provided such scheduled activities, "the residents would feel that they were being manipulated in much the same way that good-willed hospital personnel directed them."

When a referring source—usually the state hospital—has a candidate for Gilead House, the candidate is invited to come over for an evening, to meet the residents and look the house over. The director then consults both the referring professional and the residents of the house in order to decide whether or not to accept the candidate for a two-day trial visit. Following the two-day visit, all residents of the house vote on whether to accept him. During the nine months prior to our visit, all but two of fifteen applicants had been accepted. The rejections were a man who stole money during his two-day visit and a girl who was having serious family problems that threatened to interfere with her Gilead House experience.

Job preparation and placement take place in needed cases at Gilead House, often on a quite informal basis. Very few residents have been clients of the state vocational rehabilitation agency. The residents are typically referred to the director of the state employment agency, who is a member of the Gilead House board of directors. He usually personally helps them to find jobs. In contrast to some other halfway houses the residents generally do not indicate to their prospective employers that they have been hospitalized for mental illness.

Both students and ex-patients are free to socialize outside the house, of course, but in actuality most have tended to limit their social activities to fellow residents. The house feels that it has no jurisdiction over the behavior of any resident when he is away from the house, but makes it clear that behavior proscribed in the house is not to be brought in from the outside. Said Mr. Hammer:

> The rules apply equally to the students and to the residents. If one of them goes away and experiences some activity that's prohibited in the house, well, that's his business. But if such experiences are conflicting with the goals we have set for this person, if they're prohibiting him from working, if he shows a tendency to drift away from the people living in the house, then we will confront him, and he knows this.

Medication and medical service

Psychotropic medications are readily available to Gilead House residents through the outpatient department of the Connecticut Valley Hospital, located one and a half miles away. The residents can obtain prescriptions there, and, if they cannot afford to pay, can have the prescriptions filled at the hospital's pharmacy.

At the time of our visit only two of the nine ex-patients were taking such medications, and there seemed to be relatively little interest in or value placed on them. There is no requirement that the residents have either a psychotherapist or a general physician. Physical health problems are usually handled by the local general hospital and its outpatient clinic.

Outcome

The outcome of the Gilead House experience for the twelve ex-patients who left during 1969 was encouraging. Only two returned to hospital; one of these was a man who had been hospitalized 27 times previously and, during his brief stay, spent scarcely any time at the house. One returned to live with his family. Two women were living in the community and attending a day-care program. Five women and two men had moved on to independent living quarters.

The numbers involved here are of course too small to be used as an indicator of the likely future course of events at Gilead House. But even taking into account the selective intake process, these early figures are impressive—so much so that we urgently hope that Gilead House will survive and that its efforts and experiences can be adequately measured and recorded. If this rate of successful outcome can be sustained, then Gilead House will be a model of great importance for the future planning of services in the community for people with a history of mental illness.

Agency and community relationships

We have mentioned that during its early days the relationship between Gilead House and its neighbors was acrimonious. Since the "turnabout" of mid-1969, relationships have improved somewhat; they were further enhanced by a recent open house.

Dealings with Connecticut Valley Hospital have varied over time. Following an initial period of enthusiasm, the hospital began to be leery of Gilead House at that point in its development when rumors were being spread about its activities. Following the advent of Mr. Monahan and Mr. Hammer, relationships have greatly improved. The hospital provides a more-than-adequate supply of referrals—there has been a waiting list in recent months—and the administration of the hospital supports and endorses the program. The hospital superintendent is a member of the board of directors.

Wesleyan University was at least receptive enough to the idea for Gilead House to agree to rent it a house, although not at any discount. The Gilead House staff has tried repeatedly, without success, to have the psychology and/or sociology departments grant course credit for living in Gilead House; these negotiations were still bogged down at the time of our visit. All in all, the university does not seem to have gone out of its way to support and encourage Gilead House.

Financing

During its first two years, Gilead House received a grant of about $7500 per year from the Connecticut Department of Mental Health. There were small donations from the mental health association, the Connecticut Valley Hospital auxiliary, and the Wesleyan college body committee. The remainder of the budget—about two thirds—came from room-and-board fees. Both the ex-patients and the students pay a fee of $22 per week for room and board. (This is somewhat lower than the room-and-board charge at the university.)

The codirector receives free room and board but no salary. The director, until recently, has received room and board plus a salary of $300 per month. Plans were afoot to attempt to increase the director's salary to approximately $9000 per year, still a modest figure for the responsibilities involved.

Whether Gilead House will be able to find ways to supplant the mental health department grant will be an important determinant of whether the program will survive.

For what it offers, the Gilead House program must surely be one of the least expensive and most promising in the country.

XV. Transitional Services, Inc. Pittsburgh

TRANSITIONAL SERVICES, INC., a private agency that contracts to Pennsylvania's Allegheny County Mental Health and Mental Retardation Program to provide transitional housing with supportive services for people who have been hospitalized for mental illness, is possibly the country's only such private agency designed to develop such services for an entire metropolitan area.

Origins

The present large and growing organization traces its origins back to the early 1960's, when certain individuals working on the staff of a Pittsburgh settlement house sought to obtain a demonstration grant to finance a halfway house for people returning from the state hospitals. The grant request was denied on the grounds that sufficient demonstrations of the capabilities of halfway house services were already under way.

In 1963, United Mental Health Services, a citizens' planning and co-ordinating body that oversees the mental health resources of the county and is the local affiliate of Pennsylvania Mental Health, Inc., carried out a county-wide survey of the needs of people who had been hospitalized for mental illness. While it found substantial gaps in service, unfortunately for the time being there was no success in identifying sources of funds to establish these services. Two years later, the findings of the survey were summarized in a report that became the basis for an application for funds from the federal Office of Economic Opportunity. The report asserted:

> . . . particularly when the time for return to the community comes, [people who have been hospitalized for mental illness in public institutions] face economic and social barriers that affect the future course of their illness. . . . Clinical services for the patient about to be discharged from a mental hospital can be found. It is more difficult to find proper sources of help for his employment and resocialization needs. *But housing needs are almost totally unmet in Allegheny County.* . . .

A system for providing adequate housing, particularly for low-income people being discharged or on leave from mental hospitals, must be established in Pittsburgh. . . . The missing element of service for mental patients returning to community life is a mechanism to arrange for transitional housing that will serve the clinical and social requirements of the patient.

The report went on to identify the general characteristics of the population needing these services: *a*) the length of hospitalization for the majority ranges between two and nine years; *b*) they are markedly debilitated economically and maladapted socially; *c*) they are ill equipped to assume the responsibilities of daily living; *d*) most of them have poor employment histories; *e*) a high percentage are unemployed, even though about half have completed technical or professional education that could potentially be utilized. Some of the everyday skills that this population needs to acquire were identified as housekeeping, basic budget management, personal hygiene, and preparation of food. The program components envisioned included a halfway house, a system of apartments, an inexpensive commercial hotel, foster homes, and a room registry.

What may be the only mental health grant for direct services to have been funded by the Office of Economic Opportunity was awarded in mid-1966 to United Mental Health Services as the responsible agency. O. J. Royer, a social worker with extensive experience in housing programs, was recruited as project director. Of eight Pittsburgh neighborhoods defined as poverty areas, three elected to be included in this program to develop transitional living services for residents returning from the state hospitals. Within five months, the project staff had established two apartments for former mental patients in each of the three neighborhoods, and had developed a roster of thirty foster homes inspected and considered suitable for placement of people coming from the state hospitals.

But seven months after the grant was awarded, the program was advised that funding was being canceled because of a reordering of OEO priorities. Given only three weeks' notice, the program urged an additional month's grace period, which was granted. Then it set about to identify alternate sources of funds.

Early in 1967 a grant was obtained from the Maurice Falk Medical Fund, but by this time almost all of the staff had left to accept other jobs. Nonetheless, with reduced funding the program continued to develop, with the Falk Fund money later supplemented by grant-in-aid from the state Office of Mental Health to cover the base salaries of staff.

In April 1969, after having functioned as a demonstration program under the sponsorship of United Mental Health Services, Transitional Services, Inc., was chartered as a private, nonprofit, autonomous agency. In mid-1969 it contracted with the Allegheny County Mental Health and Mental Retardation Board, the local authority under Pennsylvania's community mental health act, to develop and provide transitional living services for all of the county's mentally ill and mentally retarded who appeared to need them, as funding permitted.

Physical facilities

Until a short time before our visit in March 1970 a single building had housed both the halfway house for the former mental patients and all of the offices for Transitional Services. This old, large, rambling, three-story building, located in a middle- to lower-middle-class neighborhood convenient to public transportation, had staff offices in the basement and on the third floor. The staff members have recently been relocated to an attractive suite of offices on the ground floor of a new high-rise apartment building located about three blocks away.

The first floor of the halfway house, known as Coral Center, consists of an average-sized living room, a large dining room, a small office and bedroom for the resident managers, two rooms accommodating four women residents, two powder rooms, and a full bathroom. The second floor consists of seven bedrooms that house from two to three men each, a total of fifteen, with adequate bathroom accommodations. The house seems cramped in the living areas. It gives a somewhat drab but none-theless comfortable impression.

As of the time of our visit, the program was operating sixteen apartments housing both former mental patients and the retarded. These accommodate three to five persons each. The one that we inspected was located on the upper floor of an attractive new high-rise building. It was spacious, light, and well furnished.

As of mid-1970, the program had 20 apartments housing 86 residents. Fourteen of these are in modern apartment complexes, while six are in older facilities, such as converted single family houses. The older apartments eventually will be replaced by those in newer facilities.

Transitional Services also operates a halfway house for the retarded, with a capacity of sixteen. In May 1970 it added a "supervised apartment building" that houses nineteen residents plus the resident managers in six individual apartments.

A second supervised apartment building, opened in August 1970, houses a resident couple and 24 residents in seven individual apartments.

This second building houses former mental patients as well as retarded persons. Transitional Services feels that its initial experience with this type of facility had been most favorable, in that, with supervision, a greater range of individual needs can be accommodated, varying in length of time, in a more realistic setting. Counseling and home management training are conducted in the individual apartments. Movement through the group home into the more independent setting of the apartment building is greatly accelerated, utilizing the independent apartment, if appropriate, as the final step.

The staff

At the beginning of 1970, the staff of Transitional Services was dramatically increased in size, in anticipation of a very substantial increase in caseload. The roster of staff provided to us showed 15 full-time positions and five part-time positions, plus two full-time trainees, two part-time trainees, and eleven part-time staff under the "new careers" community action program. In addition, 26 other full-time jobs were shown as vacant. Thus, assuming that this program realizes its presently anticipated eventual size, it will probably be the largest agency in the country with particular responsibility for meeting the residential needs of the mentally disabled.

Considering the size of the caseload in early 1970 (see below), Transitional Services was at that point richly staffed. For example, to take a single component, at the halfway house serving formerly hospitalized mental patients, there were a couple serving as resident managers, three counselors, one cook, and one part-time "new careers" student who assisted the counselors. The counselors have additional responsibilities, including intake of new residents and "case management" of residents living in the apartment buildings. However, the situation as of the time of our visit was a temporary one, and the size of the staff is best viewed in terms of the program's plans and aspirations for the intermediate and distant future. To illustrate the growth that had taken place and was anticipated for the future: in mid-1969 there were only 30 active cases; when we visited the program in March 1970 there were 80; the anticipated caseload for July 1970 was 140, for January 1971, 200, and by July 1971, nearly 300.

The increase in staff came about because it was felt necessary to develop a cadre of employees with professional training in mental health who would become acquainted with the program from the bottom up in anticipation of their moving on to supervisory positions. When this group has acquired an appropriate amount of experience, it is anticipated, additional staff untrained in the mental health field will be added to work under the direction of the professionals.

The staff members that we interviewed seemed to be involved with their clients and sensitive to their needs. Several trained as rehabilitation counselors were performing functions that more typically are associated with social work roles. Some of them described their activities in accompanying clients out into the community, seeing employers, teaching them how to shop, and so on. Assignments and responsibilities were largely fluid and to some degree still being worked out. No job descriptions had been developed, on the grounds that the innovative nature of the program and its goals would require a period of experimentation before the best division of duties and application of skills could be formulated.

The majority of the present staff have formal training and credentials in the mental health disciplines. Transitional Services feels that professional training, at least for those who will become supervisory, is necessary to foster harmonious and effective relationships with the agencies from which it will receive its clients and from whom it must seek a variety of different services that its clients need. A considerable number of the staff were recruited to the program directly from training. This, too, is by design. "We do more untraining than training," Mr. Royer commented in the course of describing the attributes, orientation, and frame of reference that are needed from staff members of a community-based program attempting to deal with the real life problems of people who have been institutionalized. He feels this is easier to do with younger professionals and workers without mental health experience.

The residents

Transitional Services considers its mental illness/mental retardation clients as a single group for statistical purposes, and consequently the data provided to us do not provide a specific picture of the characteristics of the mental illness residents. From our interviews with staff members it appeared that there were in fact some important differences between the two groups; for example, the majority of the mental illness residents appear to be older than the majority of the mental retardation residents. In any case, for what it is worth, some of the characteristics of the combined 157 persons who were active cases during the year prior to March 1970 were as follows.

Seventy-three percent of the men and 71 percent of the women came to the program from state hospitals or state schools, the remainder from a variety of sources, including private mental hospitals, general hospitals, the Veterans Administration, several social agencies, and psychiatrists in private practice.

Fifty-two percent of the residents were men. Seventy-nine percent of the men and 60 percent of the women had never been married. By age, 33 percent of the men and 40 percent of the women were 30 years old or younger; 40 percent of the men and 37 percent of the women were between 31 and 50; and 27 percent of the men and 23 percent of the women were 51 or older.

Among the 76 persons who were discharged from the program during that one-year period, just over a quarter—26 percent—stayed less than a month; this group consists largely of those who dropped out because they could not make the adjustment to the program. Thirty-seven percent stayed between one and six months, 30 percent between six months and a year, and seven percent longer than a year.

Most of the clients are poor. A majority receive some form of public income, from the welfare department, Social Security disability payments, and Veterans Administration pensions. Some have private sources of income, but in few cases does it exceed the welfare level. Of those who leave the program successfully because they have become employed and have been able to make autonomous living arrangements, the income level is usually higher.

An important aspect of the program is its attempt to enhance the skills of the residents in the various practicalities of day-to-day living, such as shopping, cooking, and cleaning. The staff member heading up the home economics training said that in dealing with the mental illness residents it was more often a matter of teaching these basic skills for the first time; in other words, this was not by and large a population that had at one time possessed and subsequently lost the skills of daily living, but rather were people with a lifetime history of inadequacy and impairment who were attempting for the first time to acquire the competences that would be needed in order to live in an autonomous community setting.

The program

From its very name Transitional Services suggests a spectrum of activities for former mental patients that might conceivably include housing arrangements, job training, placement, and follow-up, and medical/psychological services. In describing its intended goals, the program lists

comprehensive services leading to independent community living, including vocational counseling, placement, follow-up, casework and group-work services, homemaking training, personal loans, 24-hour "on call" services, a de-institutionalization program for long-term patients, and partial hospitalization under contract with Homestead Hospital Community Mental Health Center.

As of the time of our visit, certain of these activities were limited in extent and some were still in the planning stage.

Whatever the breadth of its activities may eventually be, it seems fairly clear that Transitional Services will not be involved with the psychiatric and medical needs of its residents. Thus far the program has accepted primarily patients who have been in institutions and who could return to those institutions should the need arise. Few are accepted who have never been hospitalized. There are more, however, who had been hospitalized previously and are accepted from the community because they appear to be at risk of rehospitalization, and it is hoped that the halfway house will serve instead. The program insists that a rehabilitation plan be set up by the referral source, in most cases with one of several outpatient and aftercare facilities in the Pittsburgh area, as well as eleven Base Service Units (community mental health center components) and approximately seven county mental health and retardation programs in the northwest section of Pennsylvania, as a condition of eligibility for service. The resident must be capable of self-medication. For those who do not have money to pay for medication, it is furnished by the clinics or through Medical Assistance.

In the vocational area, Transitional Services prefers that the hospital formulate a plan prior to the patient's leaving the hospital, often as a client of the Bureau of Vocational Rehabilitation. Its eventual activities in the vocational area do not seem to be fully defined. Even though no staff member is assigned to vocational responsibilities, the program often finds itself of necessity collaborating with residents to help them find work, particularly in cases when the initial vocational plan has failed.

The areas in which Transitional Services clearly intends to serve its clients are housing, plus training to meet the demands and exigencies of day-to-day living in the community. In carrying out its program, it is important to the agency to maintain its independence. It feels that being incorporated into any one community mental health center or government agency would limit its freedom to bring about change and test new approaches.

Transitional Services actively recruits its clients from the treating facilities. Particular staff members are assigned, in some cases for a half day a week, in other cases a whole day, to seven programs: Mayview and Woodville State Hospitals; three community mental health centers,

Western Psychiatric Institute and Clinic, Homestead Hospital, and St. Francis Hospital; and Polk and Western State Schools and Hospitals for the retarded. They do not participate in the discharge planning for all patients; for example, a hospital social worker may arrange for a particular patient to be placed directly in a foster home. But the general purpose of placing the Transitional Services staff in the hospitals is to keep the staff members aware that its services are available. Transitional Services staff members work directly with patients both individually and in groups. Most of those who become residents have already been seen by the Transitional Services staff prior to the time a hospital staff member makes the referral. Once the referral is made, the Transitional Services counselor interviews the patient, in many cases arranges for him to visit the program facilities, then writes a report indicating whether or not he seems suitable. If he does, the report is forwarded to the medical director, Dr. E. Calvin Moore, a psychiatrist who devotes an average of a day a week to the program. Dr. Moore, in most cases without seeing the applicant individually, reviews the case and makes the final determination whether he should be accepted. The program accepts most referrals and Dr. Moore approves substantially all whose acceptance is recommended by the counselor. In the program's entire history of 621 referrals, only 18 had been refused.

All of the staff members we interviewed felt that Dr. Moore's screening is of great importance, because his evaluations often serve to alert staff to problems that might arise. If Dr. Moore finds the medical management plan unsatisfactory, he has the right to call for a change or remove the resident, and in rare cases he has exercised this right. He seemed to us to be highly supportive of the program. He said that "there are many residents in Transitional Services who, I am confident, would never otherwise have been released from the state hospitals." He felt that the strong representation of rehabilitation counseling personnel on the staff was appropriate because the agency had been forced into vocational activities more deeply than had originally been anticipated.

The process of intake sometimes extends over several weeks because of the time that elapses in processing forms and because the residential facilities are sometimes filled to capacity. During this period about thirty percent of the referrals are lost through attrition; in some cases the hospital withdraws the application because of a change in the candidate's condition, in other cases the candidate decides to forego the services in favor of making his own plans.

During the crucial first weeks in the program, some residents regress, have particular adjustment difficulties that may be related to medication, and otherwise require prompt treatment service; in these cases the Transitional Services counselor attempts to arrange an immediate appointment with the treating facility that has responsibility for the resident. During the resident's entire stay, his counselor stays attuned to his treatment needs and, whenever necessary, acts as his advocate.

Placement in the halfway house, the supervised apartment buildings, and the independent apartments is often not sequential, although the program is inclined to feel that this is the preferable course. Even a brief stay in the halfway house provides a fuller opportunity to observe his capabilities, his potentiality, and his particular needs. In actuality, a large percentage of the residents are placed directly in the apartments, in some cases because of the lack of an opening in the halfway house, in other cases because their level of functioning seems to be such that they promise to do well in the less supervised apartment setting.

Within the halfway house, each resident is expected to take care of his own room and to help out in cleaning the common rooms. Although a full-time cook is employed, some residents do participate in shopping for food, preparing and serving meals, washing dishes, and cleaning the kitchen. To enhance these skills, the program engaged a home economist, who, at the time of our visit, was just completing her first "course" for the men residents. She scheduled three trips to the supermarket, the first to acquaint them with how the foods are grouped and how to read signs and labels, the second to do comparison shopping, the third to buy groceries for a particular meal; then, using a training kitchen, she and the men prepared the meal. During the six-week course, this sequence is repeated, attention is given to housekeeping chores of all kinds, and a final session is devoted to eating in a nearby restaurant.

There is no scheduled program of social or recreational activities in the halfway house, on the grounds that it is preferable to encourage the residents to become involved in the regular entertainment and cultural events of the community. The staff encourages residents to become involved in activities at the YMCA and YWCA, a nearby settlement house, their church groups, Council House, and Recovery, Inc. "Internal leisure time activities are spontaneous, just as they are in the normal household," Mr. Royer said. The spacious back yard provides opportunities for Ping-pong, croquet, and ball games, which the residents sometimes engage in with the encouragement of the house staff.

At an earlier time there were attempts to develop a "house council," but the effort was discontinued because "it led to the development of the concept of a 'patient community' that we consider inconsistent with the goals of the program."

The home economist, her assistant, and the case counselors regularly visit the residents living in the apartments, in rare cases as often as each working day, more typically on a weekly basis. The counselors are available "on call" around the clock and occasionally have to come at night to deal with an emergency—usually some practical problem such as a gas leak, less frequently with medical or psychiatric emergencies.

The home economist expressed her concern about the nutritional habits of the men in the apartments. She found that some were preparing meals limited, for example, to a can of sweet potatoes or a loaf of bread, and for this reason she was planning to develop extensive food-planning and food-preparation courses.

Transitional Services sets no limit on stay, either in the halfway house or in the apartments, preferring to make a determination based on the individual resident.

Records are kept for all residents; they include the Transitional Services referral form, a summary social history, and the report of the resident's rehabilitation plan and expectations. Significant developments are entered in the record, but by and large the staff feel that the record keeping is quite simple in comparison with that of treating facilities.

Outcome

During the year prior to our visit, 44 men and 32 women left the program. About a quarter each—22 percent of the women and 25 percent of the men—returned to the hospital. Seventy-two percent of the women and 73 percent of the men moved to autonomous living quarters. Those moving out are encouraged to find the apartments themselves, with no more staff participation than seems essential; but once the apartment has been located a staff member checks it to be sure it is satisfactory. In most cases three or four residents arrange to move out together, since most of them are living on welfare allowances insufficient to cover rentals except on the basis of sharing.

Transitional Services does not consider rehospitalization to be a failure, but rather as "something that may develop in the course of any form of illness." In most cases those rehospitalized were residents who had discontinued their medication contrary to the advice of the treating facility. In many instances, persons returning to Transitional Services a second (or even third) time are subsequently able to move on into independent community living.

Financing

For the 1969-70 fiscal year, Transitional Services operated with a budget of about $360,000, which came principally from two sources— about three quarters from the county mental health/mental retardation program, about one quarter from rents collected from the residents. In turn, most of the rents came from public third-party sources, notably welfare and disability payments to the residents.

The charge for room and board in the halfway house ranges from a minimum of $107 per month (the welfare rate) to a maximum of $150, depending on the resident's income. The charge per resident in the apartments is a flat fee of $71 per month, which includes rent and utilities. Transitional Services pays, on an average, $200 per apartment per month; most have four residents, bringing an income of $284. The remaining $84 is used to pay utilities and to defray a small part of the cost of furnishings. Rents barely meet the cost of operating the various facilities, since a considerable investment is made before the first resident is placed and one hundred percent occupancy cannot be maintained. Foundation grants and other contributions provide funds for furnishings and renovation. The program has furnished the apartments at a cost of about $3000 each. An important aspect of the agency's financial structure is its reliance on community support for capital expenditures, for such items as purchase of buildings, renovation, furniture, and equipment. Approximately $150,000 had been obtained for these purposes as of July 1970.

County funds serve to meet the costs of administration and professional services to the residents, ranging from the salaries of the staff people assigned to prepare patients within the hospital to the expense of follow-up counseling provided to people who have moved on from the program to autonomous living arrangements. During 1969-70 these expenses when divided by the amount of service rendered came to a figure of $8.86 per resident per day for administrative and professional services. This is, as Transitional Services realizes, quite high for a program whose services are essentially residential placement and resocialization. However, this figure was viewed as a temporary one, accounted for by the fact that the staff had been considerably expanded in anticipation of a much larger number of residents within a fairly short time. Mr. Royer indicated that the program believes these costs will drop to between $5 to $7 a day per resident.

For the year starting July 1970 the program anticipates greatly increased funding. With a larger number of residents, the apartment and halfway house collections are expected to increase to about $200,000, and, proportionately, the funding from the county to about $445,000. A contractual arrangement exists, providing for personnel from Transitional Services to staff a partial hospitalization program for the Homestead Hospital Community Mental Health Center, about five miles away, and this is currently budgeted at an additional $128,000. Two Model Cities grants at this time are in the final contract stages, providing a total of $275,000 additional income to establish a total of three more halfway houses and 14 more apartments. Both programs will be operational by winter of 1970. The anticipated total budget for 1970-71 is approximately $1,058,000.

XVI. Mental Health Recovery, Inc.
Belmont, California

FROM ITS LOCATION NEAR THE GEOGRAPHIC CENTER of San Mateo County, Mental Health Recovery provides an interesting program consisting of a coeducational halfway house backed up by a series of apartments and houses; an additional service is a social club which was organized to provide continuing support to those who have graduated from the residential components of the program.

Origins

The program of community mental health services in San Mateo, California, is one of the earliest established, most comprehensive, and best developed in the United States. This county program, operating under the auspices of the health department and funded under the provisions of the state's Short-Doyle legislation, has been widely reported, widely visited, and closely observed as a bellwether of community mental health services in the United States.[1]

The local mental health association nonetheless became concerned in the mid-1960's with what it saw as an important gap in service: the lack of supervised transitional living arrangements for people who had been treated for mental illness, whether in the county program or at nearby Agnews State Hospital. This concern led to the establishment of a group which, over a period of two years, laid plans to establish such a service. As the plans neared completion the committee was reconstituted as the nucleus of the board of a separate nonprofit corporation sponsoring the new facility. Charles Richmond, a social worker who was directing a halfway house in a neighboring county, was recruited to head up the new facility, working in close conjunction with Dr. Richard Lamb, a psychiatrist on the staff of the county mental health program. A suitable physical plant was located. In February 1967 the

---

[1] For a detailed description see H. R. Lamb, D. Heath, and J. J. Downing (eds.): *Handbook of Community Mental Health Practice.* Jossey-Bass Inc., San Francisco, 1969.

first residents moved into El Camino House, as the new halfway house was known.

Physical facilities

Located in a mixed commercial-residential area near the heart of Belmont, the most central city in San Mateo County, El Camino House consists of a three-level thirty-year-old building that was formerly a small apartment house. Both inside and out it gives a pleasant appearance. It is modestly but comfortably furnished.

On the main level are a fairly large living room, a large combination kitchen-dining room adequate to seat all residents at one time, a staff office, and the house manager's private apartment. On the street level are the laundry room, a recreation room, and a storage area.

The nineteen residents—twelve women, seven men—are accommodated in three apartments. One, on the main level adjacent to the living room, houses six women. The other two, on the upper level, are essentially alike; one houses six women, the other seven men. Each apartment has its own bath and a kitchen. The kitchens are not used much since the residents have their meals together in the downstairs dining area.

To the rear of the house is a very pleasant small patio and garden.

The house is located near principal bus lines. It is also close to the station for the commuter train that runs the length of the county and north to San Francisco. A shopping area is four blocks from the house.

The staff

At the time of our visit, Mental Health Recovery had a full-time staff of nine persons, plus a psychiatric consultant. The staff falls into three categories: the director and an administrative secretary who have program-wide responsibilities; three persons assigned to the halfway house itself; and four persons assigned to the series of apartments that make up the "satellite housing program" described below.

The director, Mr. Richmond, spends almost half his time in such activities as working with the board of directors and committees and providing individual and group supervision to the staff. He spends about thirty percent of his time identifying and recruiting funds for the program. The rest of his time is spent in a variety of activities such as making speeches, program planning, serving on the boards of other helping agencies, and so on.

The El Camino House program coordinator, who has a master's degree in rehabilitation counseling, is responsible for screening and evaluating referrals, coordinating with agencies and therapists in the community that refer applicants or provide needed services to residents, and counseling the residents about their problems and progress. The two house managers are a woman with a bachelor's degree and a man who has completed some college work, who alternate duty hours. They have a number of responsibilities for the day-to-day running of the house, such as shopping for food and arranging for maintenance and repair work; in addition, they are frequently engaged with the residents, particularly in the evenings, in informal counseling. The house manager's primary role "is to inculcate the high-expectation culture," a description of the program states. "In addition, it is that of being available in time of crisis, of teaching, coordinating, and being supportive."

The satellite housing program is staffed by an MSW program coordinator, an MSW social worker, a "program manager" with a bachelor's degree in social work and extensive experience in the county mental health program, and a secretary.

The psychiatrist, Dr. Lamb, spends about three hours a week with the program. He meets weekly with Mr. Richmond, is a member of the admissions committee, and assumes the "medical-legal responsibility" for the agency as required by the state's community mental health legislation. Individual staff members may call on him directly in case of emergency or any difficult management problem that arises in an area that seems to call for a psychiatric opinion.

There are also three graduate social work students from Fresno State College assigned full time for three-month block placements.

The residents

During 1969 there were 88 different persons who spent some time living in El Camino House. In some respects they resembled the residents of other halfway houses that we visited, but in respect of age spread and referral source, they showed more diversity.

More than 90 percent of the residents were in the "mental illness" category, the considerable majority of these being people who had been diagnosed as schizophrenic, mostly chronic undifferentiated type or paranoid type. The only other residents during that year were three persons with a primary diagnosis of alcohol addiction and two who had been hospitalized for drug abuse.

The women outnumbered the men by a ratio of 56 percent to 44 percent. By age the residents were younger than in any other program we visited except Gilead House; but unlike Gilead House, El Camino House does not cater exclusively to the younger client and had a few admissions who were more than 50 years old.[2] Specifically, the age breakdown for residents in 1969 was as follows:

	Men	Women
Under 21	28%	33%
21 to 30	44	35
Over 30	28	33

More of the women than the men were or had been married. Only 15 percent of the men were divorced or separated, none were currently married, and 85 percent were single. Twenty-nine percent of the women were divorced or separated, eight percent were currently married, and 63 percent had never been married.

The majority of residents stayed between one and six months. The breakdown was as follows:

	Men	Women
Under one month	24%	20%
One to three months	52	35
Four to twelve months	24	45

None stayed more than a year.

The diversity of referral sources indicates the richness of psychiatric facilities and services available in San Mateo County. Slightly less than half of the 1969 referrals (49 percent) came from the state hospital, a much lower figure than for most of the halfway houses we visited. Twelve percent each came from private mental hospitals and from the psychiatric services of general hospitals, including the San Mateo County General Hospital, whose psychiatric service is the inpatient component of the county's community mental health services. A total of twelve percent were referred by various other components of the county mental health services, particularly the day treatment center, but also from the crisis clinic and the outpatient service. Eight percent came through the juvenile probation authorities, and the remaining five percent from other sources.

Most of the residents were unemployed during their tenure at the house, few had funds available from their own savings or their parents, and the majority were thus dependent on public funds to meet the cost

---

[2] Since the time of our visit Mental Health Recovery has opened a new facility, Pedregal House, specifically to serve those from sixteen to nineteen years old.

of living at the house. About 85 percent either received funds from the welfare department or were supported by the probation department.

The program

El Camino House identifies three kinds of persons who are eligible for its services:

- Patients presently at state, county, and private hospitals who require a rehabilitation program during their initial posthospital period.

- Persons living in environments not conducive to social recovery.

- Patients receiving outpatient treatment from private therapists or agencies where the therapist feels that temporary removal from an unsuitable environment would assist his therapeutic efforts or prevent hospitalization.

The house does not accept self-referrals; it requires that each referral come from a medical or social agency or from a professional in private practice.

The house asks the referring agency to submit a written application that provides a good deal of information, including present diagnosis and mental status, a brief account of the present illness, number and length of prior hospitalizations, history of or tendencies toward antisocial behavior, type and dosage of medication and name of responsible physician, and plan for financing the halfway house fees. The prospective resident is asked to complete a three-page "orientation" sheet asking his feelings about leaving the hospital, coming to El Camino House, and so on. An "orientation, screening, and intake interview" is scheduled with the El Camino House coordinator, at which time he obtains some additional data and makes an assessment of the candidate's motivation and expectations, precautions that should be taken, and limitations and strictures, if any, in such matters as a curfew or family visits.

The process just described can take from about three to ten days. When the paper work is completed, it is submitted to the next of the weekly meetings of the admissions committee, which includes Mr. Richmond, Dr. Lamb, the house coordinator, Dr. Victor Goertzel (the program's research psychologist), and sometimes others. About 95 percent of the applicants are accepted by the committee, but some of these subsequently decline to come.

This screening and intake procedure is neither the most complicated nor the simplest among the facilities we visited. The staff seemed to feel that it is appropriate because *a*) it is important to keep out the five percent, *b*) the staff need the material in order to know how to handle the resident, *c*) the process keeps liaison open with referring agencies, *d*) it helps to orient and define for the prospective resident the agreement that he is entering into with the house, *e*) it helps anticipate problems with the resident, and *f*) it provides data that might be used in future research projects.

Among the requirements that are described either to the referring agency, the candidate, or both, are the following:

- There must be some type of satisfactory structured plan for daytime activities, such as being in a training course, working, going to school, attending a day treatment center or a vocational workshop.

- The resident must be responsible for taking his own medication.

- He must have a private therapist or an agency staff member who is responsible for prescribing and reviewing his medication and for ongoing outpatient therapy.

- He must be capable of caring for his own personal hygiene.

- He must have the means to meet the minimum financial obligation.

- He must maintain his own apartment in good order and perform a fair share of the crew work of the house. "A resident's psychiatric illness is not considered a reason for failing to observe house regulations or perform on house work crews."

- He must attend the weekly house meeting and the weekly "crew sign-up meeting."

- He must come for dinner each evening that he has not signed out.

- He must sign out if he expects to be away from the house overnight or for any extended period.

- He must behave with "normal propriety and ordinary courtesy." His behavior must be that "generally expected in the community." Ordinary courtesy means "courtesies that are ordinarily expected in a family situation." Behavior that "infringes upon the rights of other residents" is unacceptable.

- Neither alcohol nor illegal drugs are allowed in the house.

- Smoking in bed is prohibited.

- Food should not be wasted and all lights should be put out before retiring for the evening in order to keep expenses to a minimum.

- The resident terminating his stay must give at least ten days' notice.

THE RESIDENTS ARE EXPECTED, in general, to be away from the facility from about 9 a.m. to 4 p.m. on weekdays. On three evenings a week meetings are scheduled, and apart from these there is, by design, relatively little programmed activity. One of the meetings is a community meeting at which the status, progress, and problems of the house are discussed, at first with the house staff present; then the house staff leave, in order that the residents can develop among themselves the solution to any problems that have been presented, about housekeeping, the behavior of particular individuals, and so on. The house staff return, hear the solution, decide whether it is acceptable or not, and if it is not, retire again while the matter undergoes further discussion. If the residents cannot eventually find an acceptable solution, the house staff can impose one of its own, but that rarely happens.

On another evening there is a crew sign-up meeting at which are presented all of the work assignments for the following week. There are usually two people assigned to cook the evening meal, and there are crews for kitchen cleanup, dishwashing, stove and refrigerator care, maintenance of the living room, recreation room, hallways, and grounds and walks. Ordinarily each resident need not sign up for more than two crews per week. The assignment is predominantly voluntary, although there is usually sufficient group pressure to result in each assignment being allocated. Efforts are made to rotate assignments, so that each resident has a range of experiences in the responsibilities of day-to-day household maintenance that will confront him when he moves on to his own living quarters. The entire house is inspected weekly by a committee of residents.

The third scheduled event of the week is the meeting of Camino Club, described below.

Satellite housing program. An interesting and important activity of Mental Health Recovery is its satellite housing program, under which it leases houses and apartments to which residents may move from El Camino House. The furnishings are donated through community solicitation.

When particular items are needed, the program can usually obtain a small article in the local newspaper. "Usually we are deluged with enough items to fill our three-garage storage area," we were told.

At the time of our visit, there were ten houses and apartments, accommodating about thirty persons. One arrangement among these was a house shared by a mother, her three children, and a student social worker.

The practice of a sponsoring agency holding the lease on apartments has some advantages for some people with a history of mental illness. They may not be working, and even if they are may not have the credit rating to be accepted as tenants and may not have the necessary security deposit. If a leaseholder relapses and has to be rehospitalized, his obligations under the lease would pose a problem. As far as we know, this practice of agency-leased apartments has not yet become widespread. It appears to have originated with Fountain House in New York, which rented apartments for its clients in preference to starting a halfway house. It is also practiced by Transitional Services, Inc., in Pittsburgh, included in this study; this program, which has both halfway houses and apartments, evaluates each candidate in terms of whether he needs the one placement or the other. Mental Health Recovery, by contrast, tends to see the two components as sequential; each client first has a stay in the halfway house, following which he may, if the outcome is successful, either be judged able to obtain his own living quarters or to need the additional support of living in one of the program's apartments.[3]

The rents range from about $200 to $250 a month for quarters that accommodate several persons, so that the per capita share falls within the living allowance provided by the welfare department. There was some interest expressed in looking for larger units with several bedrooms, because it had been found that in units housing only three or four persons it was extremely disruptive when one of them left to return to hospital or to move on to independent living arrangements.

The thirty residents at the time of our visit were arranged into four groups, each of which meets every other week with one or more staff members. Each group has a particular individual from the staff identified as its therapist and sometimes one or two others as cotherapists. The groups discuss problems that the members have in living together, handle complaints, discuss anything that is troubling an individual, including dating, use of leisure time, and so on. Between meetings, staff members are available to individual residents by telephone call.

Some of the residents of the apartments and houses socialize together, some do not.

The houses are located in several towns along the Peninsula, but all are within a short distance of the principal north-south artery, so as to be convenient to public transportation.

---

[3] Since the time of our visit, Mental Health Recovery has also begun to place people directly into the satellite units. The determination is made by the admissions committee.

Camino Club. Camino Club is "a combination open house and social club" which meets weekly at El Camino House. Present residents, former residents, and any interested persons from the community are welcome. Its purpose is to enhance social skills. Camino Club "emanated from the needs of former residents to maintain contact with staff and friends at the house." The activities include speakers, movies, slide shows, candlemaking, demonstrations in art techniques, holiday celebrations, and dancing. The typical attendance is about ten persons living in the house, eight or nine ex-residents, and five persons from the community.

Medication and medical service

We have described the requirements *a*) that each resident must be capable of self-medication and *b*) that he must have a physician who is responsible for prescribing and reviewing medication. At a given time about eighty percent of the residents at El Camino House and about sixty to seventy percent of the people living in satellite housing are on psychoactive medication. The program feels that medication is of great importance. "We could still operate the program if there were no psychoactive drugs," Mr. Richmond told us, "but there might be many patients we could not serve in this community setting. Certainly without such medications we would take on a different character."

Oftentimes the failure to take medications as prescribed appears to be the reason why residents must return to hospital. However, the resident's refusal to follow his medication regimen is also sometimes seen as symptomatic of stress in other areas of living. "A resident might 'need' to become overtly psychotic so as to insure his return to the hospital," we were told, "but this often doesn't work; we intervene to help the resident get back on medication while at the same time try to deal with the problem that precipitated his not taking the medicine in the first place."

Outcome

If one considers graduation from El Camino House to the satellite program to be a successful outcome (as we would), then the rate of success for the women who left the halfway house in 1969 was quite high— 85 percent. For the men the rate was 65 percent, which compares favorably with some other halfway houses. Specifically, the outcomes were as follows:

	Men	Women
Moved to independent living quarters	31%	39%
Moved to satellite housing program	34	29
Returned to relatives or families	0	17
Returned to hospital	31	10
Other	4	5

The rehospitalization rate for the men is substantially higher than for the women, for reasons that are unclear but may be disclosed by the evaluation study still under way.

Agency and community relationships

Mental Health Recovery seems to enjoy a particularly good relationship with the county mental health services, which, through an NIMH staffing grant, provides part of the funds to meet the salaries of staff members in the satellite housing program. The county program is a principal source of referrals. A number of the residents participate in a variety of the components of the county program. The relationship with the state hospital seems of similarly good quality.

The experience with immediate neighbors of El Camino House has been mixed. One who was originally hostile has since become friendly and supportive. Another remains opposed to the program. There have been no problems with neighbors of the satellite housing units; generally those neighbors do not know that the residents are former psychiatric patients, and the residents "are not encouraged to tell them." Landlords and neighbors who do know or find out generally do not express any concern. Particular residents who have behaved unacceptably have been asked by landlords, with the concurrence of the program staff, to leave particular houses, but not because they have been found to be mental patients.

Financing

Mental Health Recovery operated during 1970 on a budget of $139,000.

Principal sources of income were "purchase-of-service" fees under the Short-Doyle program (36 percent) and room-and-board fees from the residents (22 percent). Another major category was funds to cover the salaries and fringe benefits of satellite housing program staff members through the provisions of the NIMH community mental health center staffing grant to the San Mateo County Mental Health Services (26 percent).

Another ten percent of the budget came from the United Bay Area Crusade (the local United Fund), figured on the agency's customary "deficit financing" formula.

The major expenditures are salaries (non-staffing grants) (37 percent), rent and maintenance of El Camino House and the apartments (20 percent), a variety of administrative expenses such as office supplies, telephone, transportation (33 percent), and food (10 percent).

GUIDELINES AND PROSPECTS

XVII. Some Aspects of Creating and Operating Halfway Houses.

.

I T SEEMS LIKELY THAT HALFWAY HOUSES will continue to grow in number, partly because of the face validity of the concept of "phased
re-entry" and partly because of the increasing concern to find less traumatizing, alienating, and expensive forms of service than traditional hospitalization. We would therefore like to draw on our experiences during
this study to comment on some aspects of creating halfway houses which
we hope will be useful to people interested in establishing new ones.

Sponsorship and funding

The principal category of halfway houses is the group created under
independent, private, nonprofit sponsorship, a category which in itself
has several subdivisions. Some have been created directly by or have
come about through the direct encouragement of particular treating institutions which wanted either to round out the options available within
their programs or wanted to experiment with the feasibility of this new
kind of facility. Others have been created by local mental health associations, both to fill a perceived gap in service and to provide the association
with a high-visibility direct-service component that would broaden the
program and thus appeal to the community. Some have been created by
particular individuals, often mental health professionals of a "maverick"
quality, who have been concerned about the plight of people discharged
from treating facilities. The second largest major category appears to be
the group of houses created as components of state Division of Vocational Rehabilitation programs. Thus far, the state departments of
mental health, local mental health authorities, and community mental
health centers have not played a major role in starting or supporting
halfway houses. There is nothing to suggest that any of these auspices
would not be appropriate for future halfway houses.

In our "free enterprise" system, the independent nonprofit halfway
house may have for some a greater appeal than the one operating directly
as one of many elements of a public mental health program. There were

several of these independent programs among the group we surveyed, and each of them prized what they experienced as a kind of freedom and flexibility that they feared might be missing if they were public facilities. They were usually free to set their own eligibility and screening criteria, to decide what kind and how many staff to use, what kinds of records to keep, and so on. On the other hand, although we visited only two programs under state auspices, we did not hear of any restrictions that were creating problems, except that the amount of paper work was thought to be excessive.

Perhaps the most pertinent point is that scarcely any halfway house, regardless of its auspices, can hope to survive without an infusion of public funds. All of the independent houses that we know of depend very largely on a variety of kinds of public support—room-and-board fees from the Division of Vocational Rehabilitation, welfare payments, Social Security disability payments, grant-in-aid from local and state mental health agencies, and so on. Even those halfway houses that have a large percentage of residents competitively employed cannot anticipate enough income from this source, since characteristically the jobs that the residents hold are fairly simple, unskilled, and therefore low-paying. Thus, one may realistically begin planning a halfway house with a consideration of where the funds will come from to make up the difference, typically substantial, between what the residents can pay and what is needed to run the house.

At this point in time the most promising agencies seem to be the state Divisions of Vocational Rehabilitation, albeit with the understanding that the regulations that these agencies operate under require them to limit the period of service. Under the most favorable provisions of the federal program of support to state vocational rehabilitation agencies, a person with a mental illness diagnosis can be supported for as long as eighteen months under a provision called "extended evaluation." In actuality, few of the state programs have opted to provide service under this arrangement, and consequently the length of eligibility is likely to be limited to the length of a particular training program, typically three or four months and rarely longer than six.

The avenues whereby a halfway house may receive vocational rehabilitation funds are several. The house may become officially accepted as "a DVR house," and then receive payment directly to cover the room-and-board payments for those residents who are clients in DVR-sponsored training programs. Some houses have their own resocialization activities approved by DVR as a "Personal Adjustment Training" program, so that in addition to the room-and-board fee the house may receive a "service" fee for each resident. In other cases, where there is no formal relationship between DVR and the halfway house, particular residents may be sponsored individually for DVR training programs, as part of which they themselves receive a check to cover living expenses, a portion of which they remit to the house to pay for room and board.

State vocational rehabilitation funds for the mentally ill have been fairly readily available in recent years. During the 1960's persons in the "mental and personality disorders" category increased considerably, and in 1968 became, nationwide, the largest category of persons considered successfully rehabilitated. As described, vocational rehabilitation agencies were listed most frequently among the halfway houses in our questionnaire survey as a "principal source" of funds. In some states, however, the state vocational rehabilitation agency will not support halfway houses. And it must be always borne in mind that, even when it does do so, DVR operates under a mandate to restore people to productivity. Despite the fact that regulations of the federal program have been broadened in recent years, many of the state agencies continue to limit their efforts to those thought to have potential for competitive employment. Thus, as promising as DVR may be in some respects as a source of funds for creating additional halfway houses, it should be realized that its support cannot be indefinite; those halfway houses that see fit to accept long-term placements must look elsewhere for funds.

The houses whose residents are financed by welfare and Social Security disability payments find that these payments are rarely large enough to cover the full per capita expense of the house and consequently subsidies must be sought, principally from soliciting the public, foundation grants, or grant-in-aid from various public sources.

The person seeking information about financing a halfway house would do well to consult Rothwell and Doniger's *The Psychiatric Halfway House: A Case Study*.[1] This book-length treatment of Woodley House, in Washington, D.C., one of the first to be established, discusses alternative approaches to financing, preparing a budget, and anticipating what income might be derived from payments by the residents. Thereafter one should probably proceed with discussions with the state and local mental health authorities, the Division of Vocational Rehabilitation, the welfare department, and the Social Security Administration, to determine under what circumstances they are able to provide financial support, and to what extent. Then he must draw up an anticipated budget

---

[1] N. D. Rothwell and J. M. Doniger: *The Psychiatric Halfway House: A Case Study*. Charles C. Thomas, Springfield, Ill., 1966.

for the house, and if there is a deficit, which there is likely to be, he must determine whether there are additional avenues of support that can be counted on to make up the difference.

We believe that a viable plan that deserves encouragement would be one under which the house sets up the mechanism to receive all the funds it can from patient collections, DVR, welfare, disability payments, private contributions, and so on, whereafter the state department of mental health underwrites the deficit. Even if only a few of the residents are people who, without the halfway house, would have to be in mental hospitals, this plan would probably represent a saving to the state, and it would guarantee the house the funds to stay in existence. Gateways in Indianapolis, described herein, has arranged in much this fashion to receive a block grant each year from the state department of mental health.

The several hundred community mental health centers that have been funded under the federal program may in time take a major part in sponsoring halfway houses. The regulations pertaining to the federal program define the halfway house as one of the components of a *comprehensive* mental health service, but do not require it as one of the *essential* elements required to be eligible for federal funding. Relatively few applicants for center grants have requested funds for halfway houses thus far, largely because their resources have been fully taxed in attaining the matching funds required to support the basic services. Since the federal support is time-limited, some programs may find themselves indefinitely plagued with the problem of maintaining funds to keep the basic services operational; others in a more favorable position could qualify to obtain NIMH staffing funds for a halfway house, provided funds were available.

I T MAY BE THAT A NEW APPROACH, both more extensive and intensive, will come about, in the form of community-wide programs to provide specialized residential arrangements and the necessary supporting services to people with a history of mental illness. The only community thus formally committed as of late 1970, to our knowledge, is Pittsburgh; there, a private nonprofit corporation, Transitional Services, Inc., is contracting with the county mental health and mental retardation board to provide residential service, in halfway houses, in supervised apartment buildings, and in regular apartments, to as many of the mentally ill and mentally retarded as funds permit. The express purpose of the program is, as soon as possible, to obtain ample funds to serve every single person needing such service. Two other programs also seem to be moving in this direction, although without the same full mandate to provide county-wide service: Mental Health Recovery, Inc., in Belmont, California, backs up its halfway house with several apartments, and Rehabilitation Mental Health Services, Inc., in Santa Clara, California, operates a network of five facilities serving various categories of people with a history of mental illness. For the future this kind of "systems approach" may be more useful in terms of expanding residential services than the hitherto highly individual "springing up" of particular halfway houses.

W HETHER PRIVATE OR PUBLIC IN AUSPICE, the halfway house should probably have a board of directors. Its purposes should be to "legitimate" the agency both to the mental health professions and to the community at large, and to help the staff get things it needs. Ideally the board should concern itself with policy and planning more than with the details of day-to-day operation. It should probably be as small in size as 's consistent with the desirable representation. Suitable members would probably consist of two or three well-known and highly regarded mental health professionals, including a psychiatrist, appropriate representatives from the agencies that commonly refer to and accept referrals from the halfway house, someone from the communications media, an official of the courts or the police department, and some laymen prominent in philanthropy and fund raising.

The population to be served

There are several options available in terms of the disabilities that a halfway house will serve, ranging from the house that chooses to accept only the "traditional" categories of the mentally ill (for the most part persons with schizophrenia, depression, and severe neurosis), to those who cater to almost any form of handicapped and marginal person. The former type would seem to be based on the theory that mentally ill people have certain problems and characteristics in common that make it appropriate to specialize; the latter would seem to assume that the handicap and marginality are more crucial considerations than the particular form that the disability takes.

There was considerable variety of clientele among the eleven programs that we visited. Four were primarily serving the "traditional" mentally ill, although once that "primary" category was met, they were generally liberal about accepting people with additional disabilities, such as physical handicaps. Two were intentionally serving alcoholics as well. One, Gilead House, serving a younger population, had relaxed its initial stricture against drug addicts and abusers and had begun, shortly before our visit, to accept a few. Two were serving the mentally retarded as well; both operated separate halfway houses, however, for the retarded, although one did mix the retarded and the mentally ill in a number of the apartments under its jurisdiction. One, Magnificat House, deliberately accepted virtually any person in need, including parolees and stranded travelers.

We did not learn, either from these programs or from anything we found in the literature, of any problems attributed to mixing various categories of disabled people, and we heard occasional expressions of advantages to having a mix. For example, the director of Magnificat House believes that "different groups can help to meet one another's needs; for example, the mentally ill can help the retarded in a way that the retarded can't help each other." The director of Transitional Services said that the practice of mixing older former mental patients in the same apartment with one or two young retarded boys "had worked out beautifully," since "the needs of the young retarded are very comparable to those of the long-term mental patients."

The most common "mix" reported in our questionnaire survey was that of mental patients and alcoholics; yet conversely the most frequently reported "exclusion" was the alcoholic. We are convinced that what these programs are concerned about is not a diagnosis of alcoholism but rather with *drinking*. Most halfway houses proscribe drinking within the house, and we found a fairly widespread concern about residents who might come in drunk and disrupt the house. We think this is what really matters, and that the house would be just as upset by a schizophrenic resident who came in drunk as by one whose primary diagnosis was alcoholism. In any case, problems of excessive drinking among residents, either in the house or outside, were rarely reported to us, and we suspect that some of the houses are overly apprehensive in this regard.

Still greater concern is felt in a number of the houses about people who use illegal drugs. This seemed to us less related to any actual problems as to the general and growing social dismay about drug users, coupled with a concern that such people would bring drugs into the house, or, even if they used them only on the outside, would bring a "drug culture" into the house. There is also some feeling that the environment the drug user needs may be quite different, along the confrontational lines of such specialized programs for drug users as Synanon and Daytop Village.

The issue of drug use was discussed at some length at our conference, particularly because it seems to be a common consideration in programs serving younger people. All of the eight programs represented at the conference said they would expel a person found using drugs in the house, and five of the eight said they would expel any person that they found to be using illegal drugs away from the house.

The alcoholic and drug addict are thus, by some houses, both feared and shunned, mainly, we think, because drinking and drug use are seen as threatening both to fellow residents and to staff. A further concern is that alcoholics and drug users may be "manipulative, sociopathic people" whose transgressions of rules and demands on staff would interfere with the program for the general run of residents.

Our data are too limited to be able to recommend whether a halfway house should serve only the mentally ill or should intermix categories. We can repeat that, to the extent these houses were mixing categories, they had not experienced any problems specifically attributable to the mix. We were not able to include in our limited sample one of the houses operated by some of the state Divisions of Vocational Rehabilitation, in which all types of DVR clients are intermixed; we hope that others will look into their experience.

Whether mixing really has advantages we are unable to say. Certainly the probable continued growth of halfway houses should allow ample opportunity for experimentation. We suspect that the two principal determinants will be *a*) the particular interest and mandate of the people and agencies starting halfway houses and *b*) the requirements and provisions of funding agencies.

Age. One of the few respects in which there may be sufficient evidence to suggest specialization is the age of residents. Of the programs responding to the questionnaire survey, several that serve late teen-agers set an upper limit in the early or mid-20's. A number of programs set a lower limit of 21 so that they are ostensibly serving an "adult" population.

Among the programs we visited, we frequently heard descriptions of problems arising from intermixing younger and older residents. In general these programs feel that older people with a long history of mental illness are less demanding, easier to work with, and have a better outcome in terms of moving to autonomous living arrangements. Younger people, in the words of one program director, "take a tremendous amount of staff energy, create a lot of friction, and make life difficult for the older residents." Another program director added that while they do mix age groups, in a halfway house accommodating 19 people they would not have more than three late teen-agers at one time. Another, whose program was operating a separate facility for teen-agers, had earlier tried mixing younger and older clients but found that "both the younger and the older groups agitated each other, and particularly the younger ones drove the older residents to distraction."

Sex. As indicated, the majority of respondents to our questionnaire survey were operating halfway houses that serve both men and women. Of the programs which we visited, only one limited itself to only one sex—the Lodge, a residential/vocational program sponsored by Fort Logan Mental Health Center, is exclusively for men. Four of the other programs serve both men and women, but in separate houses. Six programs intermix men and women in a single residence.

Of the four programs serving men and women in separate houses, Gateways in Indianapolis, one of the earliest halfway houses in the country, would still follow this pattern if it were starting additional houses. Said the director of the women's house, "We found that just to introduce the residents of the men's house as guests to the women's house shook them up so badly that it took a long time to get over the effects. A lot of the hangups of our women residents have to do with their relationships with men." Another director would prefer to have sexually integrated houses but feels it probably would not be possible because of the feelings both of neighbors and of the funding agencies. One director of a program that started separate houses for men and women and then added a specialized sexually mixed house said that "the only problem we had with a coeducational house was convincing the board of directors that it was all right."

Dr. Karl Easton said of Cobble Hill Center:

> We started out only with women, then added men, and in doing so stabilized the whole residence. The addition of men made it more natural. We had experienced a number of management problems with the women, and things got easier when we added the men.

Miss Rose Mary Badami started with a women's house in Houston, then added a second house that accommodates both men and women. She feels that the new facility has the advantage of providing a protective setting in which people who typically have had problems relating to the opposite sex can do so with a certain degree of comfort.

One of the houses serving a younger population had some initial difficulties regarding sexual behavior; as a consequence it formulated a rule explicitly forbidding sexual activities within the house and has since had no problem.

We do not have any evidence to indicate which is preferable, a house serving only one sex or a house that mixes the two. We did inquire throughout the study about any "gender related" problems, and none of the houses except the one just mentioned had had any. It appears that there is nothing to contraindicate mixing men and women in the same house, provided it is not made impractical by the sensitivities of the neighborhood and the referring and funding agencies.

The building and its neighborhood

Most of the halfway houses that we know of, and all of the ones visited in this study, are located within city limits and in most cases in close proximity to the downtown business district. In seeking a location for a halfway house it seems important to try to find what, for lack of a better term, we would call an "anonymous neighborhood," one in which people go their own way without much socializing. This situation seems most typical of intown sections of cities, where one is apt to know only a few neighbors. The facilities that we visited were in neighborhoods that ranged from lower-middle class to upper-middle class. All were convenient to public transportation, an important consideration since most of the people living in halfway houses do not have an income sufficient to maintain an automobile. Most were also situated within a short walk of a shopping center, thus making it easy for the members to take their dry cleaning, to shop for toilet articles and other personal items, and so on.

With crime greatly on the increase, it would be important in searching for a new facility to try to ascertain that the neighborhood is reasonably safe. And with a continuing deterioration of the closer-in residential sections of many cities, one should try to anticipate, particularly if the house is being purchased, whether the neighborhood will deteriorate to the point that it will be inappropriate and unsatisfactory.

Assuming that one finds a suitable neighborhood, he must then find a particular house. In general this seems difficult, since most halfway houses are planned to accommodate ten or more residents plus one or two live-in staff members, thus calling for a larger-than-average building. Both in terms of availability and cost, one may be largely limited to certain older neighborhoods where spacious private homes were built several decades ago. Several of the programs that we visited were in such settings. (We did not see any programs in post-World War II houses. Also, we did not see, and we have not heard of, any halfway houses that are operating in buildings built for them.)

Three of the programs we visited had solved the problem of finding a large residence by locating in small apartment buildings. Two of these, El Camino House in Belmont, California, and the Lodge in Denver had organized the buildings so that they were being used in effect as large single residences. The third, Roscoe House in Chicago, was still utilized as individual apartments, with each group of three residents having their own kitchen and living room in addition to sleeping quarters. A fourth program, Cobble Hill Center in Brooklyn, has as its physical plant a former YWCA building that has two hundred small single rooms for sleeping quarters plus a number of public rooms for activities and meetings. The fourteen residences operated by the remaining seven programs were all situated in former private homes.

The essential components of the house appear to be a) a kitchen large enough and well enough equipped to prepare meals for all the residents to eat simultaneously, b) a dining room similarly capable of accommodating everyone at the same time, and c) a living room with enough space for occasional parties and meetings. In addition it would be desirable to have both a recreation room and a quiet room. The bedrooms, depending on their size, can ordinarily accommodate two, three, or four residents. There should be an ample number of bathrooms. If the house is to serve both men and women, it is particularly desirable for the layout to provide some degree of separation; at all of the houses we visited that are sexually mixed, the men and women are accommodated either on separate floors, in separate wings, or in separate apartments.

Even though the very size of the house one needs may limit the choice to older neighborhoods, we think that the kind of older residence one finds there has much to recommend it. The spacious, rambling homes of the early 1900's, provided they are in reasonable condition and do not require constant repairs, may be the best choice, since they frequently have a homey, comfortable feeling. They are likely to be of a quality consistent with what the resident can afford when he moves on to his autonomous living arrangement; it would seem a mistake, as one director put it, for the residents "to live in a halfway house so fine that they would be dissatisfied with what they could afford when they leave it."

It is of particular importance to be sure that one may occupy the house legally, in conformity with zoning and occupancy regulations.

Whether the neighborhood should be prepared for the advent of the halfway house is a wide-open question. Some of the facilities we visited had made such attempts, by door-to-door visits, distributing brochures, holding open house, and so on. The results were extremely mixed. In some cases the neighbors were cooperative and welcoming, in others they banded together in opposition, and in a few cases circulated petitions against the houses. The experience of those houses not attempting to prepare the neighborhood is equally mixed. In any event, once the programs had settled in, the problems with neighbors largely abated. The most desirable state of relationship between a halfway house and its neighbors seems to be one that is polite and cordial but in a detached and uninvolved way.

Recruiting the residents

It came as no surprise to us that some of the halfway houses were running at less than capacity and that there had rarely been waiting lists. A common misconception of new types of facilities and programs is that their services will be welcomed and that they will be flooded with referrals. Their actual experience in many cases is that they are not only not flooded but actually have to go out drumming up business.[2] We believe this is the result of several factors. For one thing it takes time for word to get around that a new facility is in operation. For another, there seems to be some reticence about new facilities even of traditional kinds, and perhaps even suspicion about facilities of new kinds. Related to this is a certain allegiance to the traditional way of doing things, and a concomitant resistance to change.

Thus, a number of the halfway houses have had to invest staff time in developing referrals from the hospital personnel who do discharge planning for patients, and with personnel of community resources that come into contact with troubled people who might be suitable candidates. Typically, this is not a one-time effort but must be repeated from time to time.

Beyond this, there is the difficulty, frequently voiced to us during our visits, of educating the referring personnel to the kinds of residents that the program caters to. Several programs complained that even after some years of dealing with particular hospitals many of the persons referred were grossly inappropriate in one or more respects. Some of the houses set exclusions which the hospitals ignored. Most of the houses asked that the individual either have a vocational plan or else be eligible for some kind of vocational sponsorship, and this the referrers often neglected.

These two problems—having a sufficient flow of referrals, and having appropriate kinds of referrals—were usually not of major consequence

---

[2] In earlier studies the Joint Information Service found this situation common among psychiatric emergency services and a number of day hospitals.

but rather were sources of irritation to the halfway houses. There did not seem to be a great deal that could be done except to persist in the educational efforts and to bear with the problems. In any case, a new halfway house should be aware that it will probably have to contend with them.

Screening and intake process

The programs vary a great deal in terms of the persons they deliberately do not accept. We have indicated that there are sometimes broad exclusions, such as persons with a primary diagnosis of alcoholism. Beyond this kind of categorical exclusion, the screening appears to be principally according to two criteria: *a*) does the person appear to be able to function within such a setting, meeting the demands of the house and not seriously disrupting its process nor impinging on the rights of other residents, and *b*) does he seem to have some promise of responding favorably to the program, usually in terms of showing a potential for moving on to some more autonomous form of living. Thus, at the preliminary stage some applicants might be screened out on the basis of particular past history, for example, setting fires, participating in deviant sexual practices, or having no employment history at all. How much of a risk a particular house is willing to run depends both on its philosophy and its resources, and perhaps to some extent on how many vacancies it has at a given time.

If the applicant passes the preliminary screening process, he may simply be welcomed to the house as soon as there is a vacancy, without any further formalities, or he may have to endure a prolonged process that involves the transmission of a great deal of paper describing his past and present situation, an interview before a staff intake conference, and so on. At its most exacting, this process can, and for one or two programs does, require several weeks, during which time a considerable number of referrals may drop by the wayside.

It is also, of course, necessary for the applicant to be willing to come to the house. This part of the process may consist of no more than describing to him, while he is still in hospital, what the program offers and what it expects of him, or it may involve a visit to look the house over, or, in a few cases, an exploratory visit of two or three days. In some houses the present residents must vote favorably on the candidate in order for him to be admitted.

What impressed us most about the screening and evaluation process is the professed inability of the programs to predict who will do well and who will not. "We are just unable to predict," said the psychiatrist on the staff of one of the programs. One of the directors related the efforts through the use of standardized tests to find differentiating characteristics:

> After four years of using extensive tests, we compared twenty of the residents with the most successful outcome with twenty of the least successful, and we found the only relationship to our diagnostic testing was that the successful people tended to be a little older and had a better pre-illness work record. No other factor was really related to success. The testing simply did not predict successful outcome.

A network of three halfway houses established by a Veterans Administration hospital in Gulfport, Mississippi,[3] made a follow-up study of 65 men who lived there over a two-and-a-half-year period. The study found that "successful" and "unsuccessful" outcomes were *not* differentiated by any of the following variables:

Exact diagnosis
Age at first admission
Age at placement
Marital status
Work record
Length of (military) service
Education
Prehospital occupational classification
Previous work experience
Tranquilizers
Patient attitude at time of placement
Religion
Guardianship
Family attitude
Hospital assignment

This limited prognostic capability argues, we think, for liberal acceptance criteria. Perhaps the best plan would be for the halfway house to have to justify why it should not accept the candidate, rather than why it should. In actuality, we found that most of the programs we visited, including even those that articulated fairly extensive and stringent selection criteria and complained about the inappropriateness of referrals, accepted the considerable majority of applicants.

---

[3] F. H. Wright, H. E. Brown, J. R. MacDaniel, and F. H. Engstrom: "A Descriptive Report on 65 Halfway House Patients Over a Two-and-One-Half-Year Period," *International Journal of Social Psychiatry* 12:4:289-292, 1966.

The program

A halfway house provides at minimum *a*) a place to sleep and *b*) some arrangement for meals, either prepared for or by the residents. How much if anything more the house provides depends on its philosophy, its budget, and whether other needed services are reasonably accessible from other agencies. Some halfway houses located in areas where vocational, therapeutic, and social services are either unavailable or are felt to be unsatisfactory provide many of these things as part of their own program, and thus approach "total service" agencies rather than merely a specialized residential service.

Rules. The practice of the halfway houses we visited regarding rules varied from a complete absence of written rules and a minimum of oral ones to those that had developed formidably lengthy rules.

Apprehension may lead the directors or staff of a new halfway house to sit around contemplating problems that could arise and devising rules intended to head them off. A preferable course, it seems to us, is to start out with minimal rules, limited only to those particular behaviors that can be assumed to pose a threat both to the house and to the resident. Then, if experience dictates the need for additional rules, they can be added. Some of the rules that we think are basic and essential are as follows.

1. *There must be no illegal drug use in the house.* We found that it had not occurred to some halfway houses located in areas where there is not yet much of a drug abuse problem to formulate such a rule. However, since drug abuse appears to be a growing problem, and one that is spreading to new parts of the country, it may become an important consideration, particularly for halfway houses serving younger patients.

2. *Limits should be set on sexual activities within the house.* Many of the kinds of people who need the service of a halfway house are insecure, apprehensive, and troubled about their own sexual nature and activities. Consequently, sexual activities should not be permitted between residents, nor should residents be allowed to bring in outsiders for sexual purposes. (Ordinarily we would maintain that sexual activities outside the house are the personal business of the resident, unless, of course, it appeared to a counselor or therapist that a particular relationship was destructive.)

3. *There must be no use of alcohol within the house.* This rule obtained at all of the houses we visited, except one where the stricture was limited to "no drunkenness in the house." The grounds for it seem evident enough in the case of houses that are accepting alcoholics, who

must abstain altogether from drinking. For houses accepting only the traditional mentally ill, the need to prohibit alcohol outright seems less compelling, since it is widely accepted in our culture to serve beer at a party or wine at a holiday dinner. We suspect that the prohibition against alcohol in most halfway houses stems from the uneasiness of funding agencies, boards of directors, and staff. Whatever arguments one might muster that the mentally ill should be just as entitled to engage in social drinking as other people, we suspect that at the present time it is realistic and perhaps essential to rule out drinking within the house. It also seems necessary to prohibit coming home drunk; this might be dealt with as an individual problem, but one which, if persisted in, could lead to expulsion.

4. *Residents must have an approved plan of daytime activities.* This would not apply to residents accepted for terminal placement—those who are too old, too frail, or too disorganized to be expected to work. For other residents it seems appropriate to require a planned program for weekdays. Particular residents might be going to training programs, looking for work, working in a sheltered workshop, working as volunteers in some service agency, attending a day hospital, or regularly employed. In any case, it seems inappropriate to allow residents to lie idle around the house.

5. *Residents must contribute to the maintenance of the house.* We will describe below some of the approaches to resident participation in taking care of the house. Whatever demands a particular house decides to make, each resident should be required to do his share.

6. *There must be no exploitation of one person by another.*

Demands on residents. Because of the hope that residents will become enabled as a result of their residence in the halfway house to move on to autonomous living arrangements, it seems suitable that the experience of living in the house be designed to impart what one director called "the survival skills" that are needed to meet the day-by-day demands of living on one's own.

All of the houses we visited except one required the residents to keep their individual rooms reasonably neat and clean; the other, catering to a younger clientele, imposed no regulation except that the room must not be so dirty or cluttered as to pose a health or fire hazard. We think the majority are right—that all bedrooms should be kept tidy and clean.

All of the houses except one required that each resident do his personal laundry and look after his own dry cleaning, a requirement that seems reasonable.

Beyond this, the houses differed a great deal in what was required of the residents. Most had some system of assigning such jobs as cleaning the living room and bathrooms, setting and clearing the table, helping with the shopping and cooking, taking care of the grounds, and so on. A few larger programs, such as Transitional Services in Pittsburgh, have formalized some of these activities into "courses," whereby a staff member plans meals with small groups of residents, takes them to the grocery store, and then oversees the preparation of the meal. In most halfway houses, however, these activities take place informally. If there are houseparents, they can provide guidance, supervision, and, to the extent that it is needed, inspection.

One means of dividing the work is to draw up a list of all duties, assign a unit of time to each (for example, one and a half hours for washing the dinner dishes), add up all the time units, divide by the number of residents, and then assign each resident responsibilities that account for his time contribution. The question arises of whether the residents should be allowed to do those things they prefer to do and feel most adequate and comfortable with; this would seem a fair and considerate plan. On the other hand, the residents may need experience doing exactly those things that they feel least comfortable with. Perhaps a good compromise is to require that duties be shifted from time to time, so that each resident will get some experience with a variety of kinds of responsibilities involved in day-to-day management of a household.

An area of potential complication is meal preparation. If the halfway house is small, with perhaps no more than eight or ten residents, it may be realistic to require, as is done by two of the programs we visited, that each resident take his turn cooking. (These houses admitted that the meals were sometimes not very satisfactory but felt that this was less important than giving the resident the experience.) In a larger house, food preparation becomes a major undertaking, and it may be unrealistic to expect a resident to cook for so many people. One plan would be for the houseparent to take the principal responsibility but to enlist one or more residents as "cook's helpers."

Medication and other therapeutic services. The programs vary greatly from one to another in regard to their requirements and arrangements for supervision and follow-up of medication, for counseling, psychotherapy, and so on. The importance that they attach to these aspects of service to the mentally ill also varies greatly.

Of the programs we visited, four expressed the belief that it would be possible for their halfway houses to operate even if the "psychoactive" drugs had never been developed. The others feel that the drugs are of moderate to essential importance, and several directors told us that they believe the principal reason why residents have to return to hospital is because they have neglected to stay on the medication regimen prescribed for them.

Our questionnaire survey indicated that 34 percent of the respondents had psychiatrists on their staffs, a much higher figure than we had anticipated. The majority of these are shown as working for the halfway houses only a very few hours a week, often as consultants, but we assume that they are involved largely with supervision of medication. Three of the programs that we visited had part-time staff psychiatrists who were overseeing the medication of some or all of the residents. Two of these three psychiatrists expressed their concern that some of the community clinics and hospital aftercare programs supervising the follow-up of some of the residents grossly overprescribe; therefore, the psychiatrists frequently take over the medication supervision for these residents and greatly reduce the dosage.

The residents of the halfway houses are involved in a broad variety of therapeutic activities. A number go to outpatient clinics and community mental health centers for counseling and group and individual psychotherapy. Many are seen in counseling sessions by vocational rehabilitation counselors. A few attend day hospitals while they are becoming adjusted to the house and are formulating a vocational plan. Some of the houses have group therapy sessions conducted by their own staff members, and some provide formal, scheduled individual psychotherapy and counseling to all residents.

It is impossible to say what the "best" course would be, since this will depend on the needs of individual residents and on the availability and quality of treatment and follow-up services in the community. In any event, we found ourselves unwilling to recommend that each resident should be required to be under the care of a psychiatrist or to have a "primary therapist." Not all of the people who have been hospitalized for mental illness require being in treatment all the time. The house itself, however, should have access, if not as part of its own staff, then through some affiliation or liaison, to the services of a mental health facility which would be available in case of emergency.

Vocational services. In many parts of the country, it is now relatively simple to arrange sponsorship through the state Division of Vocational Rehabilitation for people with a history of mental illness. Typically this sponsorship covers assessment and evaluation, plus a training program if one seems indicated; in some localities it also includes job finding and placement, but in other areas it does not. In some places the state employment agency has a special desk for recruiting jobs for handicapped people including the mentally ill.

In any case, since becoming gainfully employed is a principal goal for a great many of the people who live in halfway houses, each house should give a great deal of attention to a plan for getting work for its residents. Some houses have their own staff members responsible for recruiting jobs from employers willing to take a chance with people with a history of mental illness. Provided the halfway house can find the funds to pay for such a staff position, this direct approach may have much to recommend it; even if the services of the Division of Vocational Rehabilitation and the state employment agency are of good quality, there will still be residents who need special help, or who require particular intervention after an original vocational plan has failed. Several programs have successfully relied on members of the board of directors to line up jobs for residents.

Social and recreational program. The halfway houses that we visited range in the extent of social and recreational programs from moderate downward. All of them felt that it was inappropriate to provide any extensive program of entertainment and social events, on the grounds that it would be incompatible with the effort to simulate real-life conditions as much as possible, and also on the grounds that it was more in the resident's interest to try to motivate him to participate in the customary social, recreational, and entertainment activities of the community.

This is not to say that there were not special events at appropriate times, as on holidays and birthdays. But the houses more often scheduled trips to the movies, to sports and musical events, and a variety of other activities out in the community than they provided internal social events.

Aftercare. Halfway houses vary in their arrangements for service to former residents. The necessity for including former residents in one's program will depend largely on the availability and the quality of follow-up services from other resources in the community. It will also depend on the particular needs of given individuals. Some houses have formal group meetings either limited to former residents or intermixing present and former residents. Some of the houses schedule social events, usually infrequently, such as once a month, to which former residents are welcome. It was our impression that most residents who have moved on to more autonomous living arrangements do not have a great desire to make frequent return visits, so that even the most welcoming halfway house probably would not find itself burdened with former residents.

Staffing a halfway house

The kinds and numbers of staff needed for a halfway house will depend, of course, both on size and on how much service it provides beyond room and board. For present purposes, let us assume that the size of the house will be in line with the majority of the respondents to our questionnaire survey, namely between eleven and twenty people, and that treatment and vocational services of good quality will be readily available from other agencies in the community.

A first question might be whether any live-in staff are needed at all. Among the programs we visited, two, the Lodge in Denver and Roscoe House in Chicago, had no live-in staff, and they did not seem to have had any problems resulting therefrom. However, the Lodge has a superb backup from the professional staff at Fort Logan Mental Health Center, and each resident at Roscoe House has an individual case manager who can be telephoned at home at night in case of emergency.

As exciting as the idea of running a halfway house without live-in staff may be, we believe, at this point in time, that it is necessary to have at least one person residing at the house. He or she could supervise such day-by-day requirements as shopping, menu planning, cooking, and cleaning, ideally involving the residents so that their own skills will be enhanced. Some houses, particularly those of larger size, may find it preferable to have a couple as houseparents. The most likely candidates seem to be older couples who have reached retirement age. The woman should be a good cook and housekeeper, and ideally the man should be adept at some of the simpler maintenance problems that are apt to arise.

It also seems important to have a relief houseparent. From our interviews we gathered that it is unrealistic to expect the houseparents to be on the premises seven days a week. They should have two full days off, and ideally would have their own residence they can repair to. This will mean engaging a relief houseparent, who might either be an older person near retirement age, or, as McKinney House in New Orleans has arranged, a graduate student. In fact, the student might live in the house full time as a kind of "role model" and then be in charge on the two days the houseparents are away.

Another interesting possibility is the use of former state hospital patients as house staff. Magnificat House in Houston has successfully worked out such an arrangement.

In any case, it is difficult to see why more than two live-in staff, plus relief, would be needed for a house with as many as twenty residents. The directors of the programs we visited were unanimous in the view that live-in staff should not be mental health professionals. Said the director of Transitional Services, "I would never hire a house couple who had training, nor would I hire anyone to live in who had ever worked in an institution; these are two absolute disqualifications for our program."

(An important counterexample is seen in the rehabilitation houses affiliated with Vermont State Hospital, where couples formerly employed as attendants in the hospital have successfully functioned as houseparents for some years. Dr. Walter Barton comments, "There are all kinds and qualities of institutions; a well-chosen couple from an enlightened institution might make good houseparents.")

The numbers and kinds of staff not living in the house varied greatly from program to program. We could not help feeling that, as one director put it, "the house gets staffed to the extent that funds are available." In other words, since there are no standards or norms for staffing a halfway house, there seems to be an unfortunate tendency for the houses to take all the staff they can get. This tendency needs to be discouraged, not only because it increases the cost of service but also because a larger staff seems almost inevitably to take away from the residents some of the responsibilities that it is very much in their interest to carry.

The program directors agreed that the "backup" staff should be professionally trained, since their responsibilities will be largely in the recruitment and intake of residents, in dealing with a variety of community agencies around the problems of the residents, and in acting as case managers. If we assume that each resident requires an average of two hours a week of service, then a house with fifteen residents will require less than one full-time professional.

We believe that this is probably the minimum staffing requirement for the majority of halfway houses. To the extent that other kinds of services such as job finding and placement are provided, additional staff members may be needed. The halfway house might consider, however, whether a variety of additional activities could be combined into a single job, or whether part-time people could be recruited. For example, in metropolitan areas that are fairly rich in mental health resources, it is often possible to identify particular professionals who would be able to work a few hours or a day each week performing some specialized service.

Records

The programs we visited varied in their records from a one-page intake form asking a few basic questions to records more complete, more elaborate (and of better quality) than those of many medical treatment resources that we have visited. But to our minds, there is a major question regarding the usefulness of elaborate records. If they cannot be avoided because of the requirements of funding agencies, that is one thing; but otherwise, unless there were intentions of carrying out some research that would require them, we could not understand the interest in or the justification for the time required to keep extensive records.

XVIII.   The Future of Halfway Houses

IN 1965 LANDY AND GREENBLATT [1] said:

> It is not likely that [halfway houses] will ever provide appropriate rehabilitation for the large masses of emotionally impaired persons who annually either leave our hospitals, are readmitted to them, or are about to enter them for the first time. But [the] possibilities are numerous and there is every indication that the future of social psychiatry in this country will depend in part upon their further development and expansion—in numbers, rather than necessarily in size.

Since that was written, the numbers have in fact increased dramatically, and if the rate of creating new facilities as of mid-1969 were to hold up, by the end of this decade there would be some hundreds of halfway houses. It is possible, of course, that the rate will increase. Yet if the time were to come that as many as 100,000 of the half million who are now inpatients were to be living in halfway houses, there would need to be about 5,000—more than 25 times the present number. Many contingencies will determine whether this "movement" can grow to such dimensions.

Having had the opportunity of observing almost a score of houses operated by eleven programs, we find ourselves hoping that the growth will not only continue but will accelerate. We believe that except under the most extraordinary circumstances it is better to be living in the community than in a hospital, that it is better to be productive than to be idle, and that it is a good thing to derive some meaning and satisfaction from life. For many of the people with a history of serious mental illness, we believe the halfway house is one important means of realizing these goals.

---

[1] D. Landy and M. Greenblatt: *Halfway House: A Sociocultural and Clinical Study of Rutland Corner House, a Transitional Aftercare Residence for Female Psychiatric Patients.* U.S. Department of Health, Education, and Welfare, Washington, D.C., 1965.

APPENDIXES AND
BIBLIOGRAPHY

Identifying Questionnaire to Halfway Houses

1. Do you accept persons who are or have been mentally ill as residents in your halfway house? __Yes __No
(If "No," please sign and return this questionnaire.)

2. Do you accept any other categories of persons as residents in your halfway house? __Yes __No
(If "Yes," please specify.)

3. In what year did your halfway house begin operation? _____

4. What is the capacity? ____men ____women ____either sex, as needed.

5. Do you set any age limit? __Yes __No
If "Yes," please indicate: Lower limit_____ Upper limit_____

6. Do you exclude any particular categories of persons who are or have been mentally ill? __Yes __No
(If "Yes," please specify.)

7. During the current year to date, how many different persons have resided in your halfway house? _____mental illness residents _____other residents.

8. Under what auspices does your halfway house operate?
_____state government _____local government _____private nonprofit _____private for profit.

9. What is your minimum monthly charge to residents?_____ Maximum charge?_____

10. What are the two or three principal sources of funds?

11. If you provide or sponsor any services or programs other than sheltered residential placement, please describe the other activities.

12. If you are in any way related to or affiliated with a federally assisted community mental health center, please describe the relationship or affiliation.

13. What are the principal sources from which mental illness residents are referred to you?

14. Please list the staff currently working in your program.

Job title	Highest degree	Number of hours worked per week

Orientation Questionnaire to Halfway Houses Visited

We prefer that you base your answers to the following questions on Calendar Year 1969. However, if you already have some of the data collected and available for some other recent period, please use that rather than recompute. In either case, please indicate here the period used for answering these questions: _____

1. How many "mental illness residents" resided in your halfway house during the period indicated above? _____

2. How many "non-mental illness residents" (if any) resided in your halfway house during the same period? (Do NOT include staff) _____
Please describe the kinds and numbers of each kind of "non-mental illness residents."

3. Please provide, for all the persons who resided in your halfway house during the above period, a breakdown by age, sex, and marital status, as follows:

	Under 21	21-30	31-40	41-50	51-60	Over 60
Single men	—	—	—	—	—	—
Married men	—	—	—	—	—	—
Divorced, separated men	—	—	—	—	—	—
Single women	—	—	—	—	—	—
Married women	—	—	—	—	—	—
Divorced, separated women	—	—	—	—	—	—

4. For those residents who left your halfway house during the above period, please indicate the length of stay, as follows:

	Under 1 wk.	1 wk.- 1 mo.	1-3 mos.	4-6 mos.	6 mos.- 1 year	Over 1 year
Men	____	____	____	____	____	____
Women	____	____	____	____	____	____

201

5. Do you set a limit on length of stay? Yes___ No___
   If "yes," what is the limit? _____
   How did you arrive at this limit?

6. For persons who resided in your halfway house during the above period, please indicate referral sources, as follows:

	Number men	Number women
State hospitals	_____	_____
General hospitals	_____	_____
Private mental hospitals	_____	_____
Psychiatrists in private practice	_____	_____
Other (please specify):		
_____	_____	_____

7. If you provide any scheduled or fairly regularly occurring social activities, please describe.

8. If you have any liaison with sheltered workshops or regular employers, or if in any other way you help residents to find jobs, please describe.

9. If there is a "patient government" or a house council, please describe.

10. If you keep records on the residents, please describe the contents and how they are maintained.

11. Please provide any data you have, or, if you have none, your impressions about the income and financial status of the persons who have been residents during the same period as above.

12. What requirements do you have that a resident be under the care of a mental health professional? How are medications obtained by the residents?

13. For residents who left your halfway house during the period used in answering the earlier questions, please indicate where they went, as follows:

	Men	Women
Returned to hospital	_____	_____
Returned to relatives or families	_____	_____
Went to some other "sheltered" residence	_____	_____
Moved to independent living quarters	_____	_____
Unknown	_____	_____
Other (please specify):		
_____	_____	_____

Directory of Halfway Houses

| Name and Location | Year opened | CAPACITY | | | Clients served* | Age limits |
		Male	Female	Either		
Rehabilitation House, Inc. Birmingham, Ala.	1966	—	X**	—	MI	16+
CAN Enterprises, Inc., Domiciliary Mobile, Ala.	1969	16	—	—	MI, Alc, O, PH	16–65
Elks Memorial Center Montgomery, Ala.	1961	45	47	92	MI, PH	16+
Goode Street Facility Montgomery, Ala.	1965	20	20	—	MI, PH	Adults
Sayre Street Facility Montgomery, Ala.	1964	12	10	—	MI, PH	Adults
Gaines House, Inc. Little Rock, Ark.	1967	—	22	—	MI	—
Mental Health Recovery, Inc. Belmont, Calif.	1967	2	11	—	MI, Alc, DU	18+

Alc—Alcoholic   O—Offender
PH—Physically Handicapped   DU—Drug User

*MI—Mentally Ill
MR—Mentally Retarded
**Indicated category, but not number.

Directory of Halfway Houses (Continued)

Name and Location	Year opened	CAPACITY			Clients served*	Age limits
		Male	Female	Either		
Gateways Hospital and Community Mental Health Center Los Angeles, Calif.	1953	—	—	60	MI	15+
Miramonte Mental Health Services Palo Alto, Calif.	1963	—	—	12	MI,Alc,DU,O	16+
Baker Place San Francisco, Calif.	1964	12	10	—	MI	17-45
Conard House San Francisco, Calif.	1959	14	14	—	MI	18-35
Community Care Home San Jose, Calif.	1964	6	6	—	MI	—
Quarters for Women San Jose, Calif.	1961	—	9	—	MI	—
Quarters for Men Santa Clara, Calif.	1956	7	—	—	MI	—
Men's Co-op House Boulder, Colo.	1967	6	—	—	MI, Alc	17+

Facility	Year				Type	Age
Women's Co-op Home (of Mental Health Center) Boulder, Colo.	1969	—	4	—	MI	—
Opportunity House Colorado Springs, Colo.	1966	18	—	—	MI, PH, MR, O	—
C.O.R.P. Apartments Ft. Logan Mental Health Center Denver, Colo.	1968	—	—	18	MI	18+
Ft. Logan Mental Health Center Denver, Colo.	1962	—	—	30	MI	18+
Labor Saver Service, Inc. Denver, Colo.	1967	18	—	—	MI, Alc	—
Rehabilitation House for Men Denver, Colo.	1960	32	—	—	MI, Alc, O	—
Rehabilitation House for Women Denver, Colo.	1960	—	14	—	MI, Alc, O	—
Bridge House, Inc. Grand Junction, Colo.	1964	16	4	—	MI, Alc, DU, MR	—
Rehabilitation House for Men Pueblo, Colo.	1962	25	—	—	MI, Alc	14+
Rehabilitation House for Women Pueblo, Colo.	1962	—	15	—	MI, Alc	14+

Directory of Halfway Houses (Continued)

Name and Location	Year opened	Male	Female	Either	Clients served*	Age limits
			CAPACITY			
Niles House Hartford, Conn.	1966	—	16	—	MI	20+
Gilead House Middletown, Conn.	1968	9	6	—	MI	18-25
New Haven Halfway House, Inc. New Haven, Conn.	1967	—	—	15	MI	—
The Herman J. Bennett House Wilmington, Del.	—	14	8	—	MI	—
Anchor House Washington, D.C.	1966	10	6	—	MI	25-55
Kalorama House Washington, D.C.	1969	6	6	—	MI, Alc, DU	16-65
Woodley House Washington, D.C.	1958	10	10	—	MI	—
Gateway Residence, Inc. Jacksonville, Fla.	1963	17	17	—	MI	Employable
Sunrise House Sarasota, Fla.	1964	—	20	—	MI	—

Name and Location	Year				Diagnosis	Age
Albany Rehabilitation Residence, Albany, Ga.	1966	4	12	—	MI, Alc, DU	17+
Female Rehabilitation Residence, Atlanta, Ga.	1965	—	15	—	MI	—
Male Rehabilitation Residence, Atlanta, Ga.	1965	15	—	—	MI	16+
Vocational Rehabilitation Residence, Atlanta, Ga.	1965	15	—	—	MI	—
Augusta Rehabilitation Residence, Augusta, Ga.	1967	4	12	—	MI	—
Columbus Rehabilitation Residence, Columbus, Ga.	1966	6	10	—	MI, Alc	16-60
Savannah Rehabilitation Residence, Savannah, Ga.	1968	—	15	—	MI, Alc, MR	16-60
Elgin Transitional Care Program, Elgin, Ill.	1966	45	—	—	MI	18+
Gateways for Men, Indianapolis, Ind.	1967	11	—	—	MI	17+
Gateways for Women, Indianapolis, Ind.	1958	—	14	—	MI	17+
Halfway House for Men in St. Joseph County, South Bend, Ind.	1968	12	—	—	MI	—

Directory of Halfway Houses (Continued)

Name and Location	Year opened	CAPACITY			Clients served*	Age limits
		Male	Female	Either		
River Heights Halfway House Sioux City, Iowa	1960	—	—	20	MI, MR	18+
Meadowlark Homestead, Inc. Newton, Kans.	1965	—	—	26	MI	18-60
Stepping Stone Lexington, Ky.	1962	—	8	—	MI	—
Colonial Inn Louisville, Ky.	1961	—	8	—	MI, Alc	Employable
Baton Rouge Halfway House Baton Rouge, La.	1967	10	—	—	MI	16+
McKinney House New Orleans, La.	1964	12	—	—	MI, Alc, PH	18+
New Orleans Halfway House for Women New Orleans, La.	1969	—	11	—	MI, Alc, PH	18+
Fellowship House, Inc. Baltimore, Md.	1969	9	9	—	MI	17+
Boston State Hospital Boston, Mass.	1968	—	—	77	MI	—

Facility	Year				Type	Age
Brooke House, Boston, Mass.	1965	25	—	—	MI, O	17+
Everett House, Boston, Mass.	1954	—	12	—	MI	12-17
Halfway House, Boston, Mass.	1968	6	4	—	MI	18+
Cooperative Apartments—Brookline Mental Health Center, Brookline, Mass.	1963	—	5	—	MI	—
Rutland Corner House, Brookline, Mass.	1954	—	13	—	MI	18+
Prospect Hall, Fall River, Mass.	1969	—	8	—	MI	16-24
Gould Farm, Great Barrington, Mass.	1913	—	—	X**	MI	16-60
Wild Acre Inn, Inc., Lexington, Mass.	1965	—	—	24	MI	21-60
Grafton Venture Corporation, North Grafton, Mass.	1969	—	—	17	MI	—
West Street Cooperative House, Somerville, Mass.	1967	—	—	6	MI	—
Downey Side, Inc., Springfield, Mass.	1967	X**	—	—	MI	—

Directory of Halfway Houses (Continued)

Name and Location	Year opened	CAPACITY			Clients served*	Age limits
		Male	Female	Either		
Kansas City Halfway House Foundation Kansas City, Mo.	1966	7	8	—	MI	15—Employable
Opportunity House Concord, N.H.	1967	8	6	—	MI	16-50
Overing Apartments Bronx, N.Y.	1964	6	10	—	MI	18+
Cobble Hill Center Brooklyn, N.Y.	1966	20	180	—	MI	18-55+
Harmony Halfway House Brooklyn, N.Y.	1967	37	16	—	MI	—
Bierer House New York, N.Y.	1963	—	—	X**	MI	—
St. Lawrence State Hospital Ogdensburg, N.Y.	1968	—	15	—	MI	15-59
East House Corporation Rochester, N.Y.	1967	8	10	—	MI, Alc	18+
Dominion House Schenectady, N.Y.	1968	—	9	—	MI	18-65

				X**		
St. Josephs Psychiatric Services Syracuse, N.Y.	1969	—	—	X**	MI	16+
Futura House Foundation, Inc. White Plains, N.Y.	1968	—	9	—	MI	21+
Charlotte Rehabilitation House Charlotte, N.C.	1967	—	—	23	MI, MR	—
Durham Rehabilitation House for Men Durham, N.C.	1967	11	—	—	MI, MR	16+
Durham Rehabilitation House for Women Durham, N.C.	1966	—	14	—	MI, MR	16+
Guilford Rehabilitation House, Inc. Greensboro, N.C.	1965	11	10	—	MI	16+
Guilford Rehabilitation House, Inc. High Point, N.C.	1965	12	—	—	MI, MR	18—Employable
Forsyth Rehabilitation House Winston-Salem, N.C.	1968	—	11	—	MI, MR	—
Tarry House Akron, Ohio	1967	5	6	—	MI	18-55
Gutman House Portland, Oreg.	1962	7	—	—	MI	18-65
Norristown State Hospital Norristown, Pa.	1958	—	26	—	MI	—

Directory of Halfway Houses (Continued)

| Name and Location | Year opened | CAPACITY | | | Clients served* | Age limits |
		Male	Female	Either		
Horizon House West Philadelphia, Pa.	1960	17	6	—	MI	17+
Rebecca Gratz Club Philadelphia, Pa.	1960	—	30	—	MI	17-35
Transitional Services, Inc. Pittsburgh, Pa.	1967	15	4	—	MI, MR, Alc, DU	—
Threshold of Berks County, Inc. Reading, Pa.	1967	—	9	—	MI, MR	18-65
"Prep" House Aiken, S.C.	1969	12	—	—	MI	—
Hilltop House Nashville, Tenn.	1966	11	—	—	MI	—
Amarillo Mental Health Friendship House Amarillo, Texas	1968	10	4	—	MI, MR	18-65
Mary Lee School of Special Education Austin, Texas	1963	—	48	—	MI, MR	14-35
Big Spring Halfway House, Inc. Big Spring, Texas	1960	—	—	12	MI, MR, Alc	—

						16—Employable
Chaparral House Corpus Christi, Texas	1968	—	—	15	MI, MR	16—Employable
Town House G., Inc. Dallas, Texas	1967	—	9	—	MI, MR	16+
Turtle Creek Manor Dallas, Texas	1968	—	—	30	MI, MR	16-60
Casa Blanca El Paso, Texas	1968	—	—	20	MI, Alc	17-60
Magnificat House I Houston, Texas	1968	—	12	—	Anyone in need	—
Magnificat House II Houston, Texas	1969	20	4	—	Anyone in need	—
Sancta Maria Hostel Houston, Texas	1963	—	9	—	MI, O, Alc	—
Lubbock Halfway House Lubbock, Texas	1968	—	—	15	MI, MR	16+
Marbridge Odessa, Texas	1968	—	—	15	MI, MR, Alc, DU	16-65
Halfway House of San Antonio San Antonio, Texas	1963	20	20	—	MI, Alc	16+
Alpine House Provo, Utah	1963	8	6	—	MI, MR	17-55

Directory of Halfway Houses (Continued)

Name and Location	Year opened	CAPACITY			Clients served*	Age limits
		Male	Female	Either		
Irons Rehabilitation Center— Vocational Rehabilitation Division Burlington, Vt.	1958	6	6	—	MI	16+
Spring Lake Ranch Cuttingsville, Vt.	1932	22	13	—	MI	15+ (physically mobile)
Irons Rehabilitation Center— Vocational Rehabilitation Division Montpelier, Vt.	1956	6	6	—	MI	16+
Seattle Mental Health Institute Seattle, Wash.	1968	—	—	23	MI	—
Division of Vocational Rehabilitation House Huntington, W.Va.	1960	12	—	—	MI, MR	16+
Division of Vocational Rehabilitation House Huntington, W.Va.	1960	—	12	—	MI, MR	16+
Weston Rehabilitation House Weston, W.Va.	1966	20	20	—	MI	—
Fulton Hall Eau Claire, Wis.	1965	—	—	17	Anyone in need	18+

Paquette House, Inc. Fond du Lac, Wis.	1967	6	6	—	MI, MR, PH, Alc	18+
Bridge Manor Green Bay, Wis.	1969	—	—	32	MI	—
Rock County Halfway House Janesville, Wis.	1967	6	—	—	MI, MR, Alc	—
Rock County Rehabilitation Services, Inc. Janesville, Wis.	1967	6	—	—	MI, MR, PH	17+
Siena Hall La Crosse, Wis.	1967	12	8	—	MI, MR	17+
Leigh Roberts Halfway House Madison, Wis.	1964	—	16	—	MI	21-50
Social Adjustment Center Madison, Wis.	1964	12	—	—	MI, MR, PH	21+
Holiday House, Woerfel Hall Manitowoc, Wis.	1967	—	8	—	MI, MR, PH	18-35
Maple Manor Marshfield, Wis.	1969	—	—	12	MI, Alc, DU	18+
Chapman House Milwaukee, Wis.	1969	—	18	—	MI	21+
Herold House Milwaukee, Wis.	1969	—	6	—	MI	—

Directory of Halfway Houses (Continued)

Name and Location	Year opened	CAPACITY			Clients served*	Age limits
		Male	Female	Either		
Snyder House Milwaukee, Wis.	1969	—	16	—	MI	21+
Rehabilitation House, Inc. Neenah, Wis.	1963	4	8	—	MI, MR, Alc, O, DU	18-65
Gateway House Racine, Wis.	1964	—	—	16	MI, Alc, O	18-65
The Abode Sheboygan, Wis.	1967	—	—	6	MI, Alc, O, MR	18+
Nelson House Waukesha, Wis.	1968	—	—	X**	MI	—

Selected Annotated Bibliography of Psychiatric Halfway Houses

Compiled by Linda Beth Parker

BARTON, W. E., *Administration in Psychiatry*. Springfield, Illinois, Charles C. Thomas, 1962, pp. 65, 158-160, 174, 516, 656.
General description of halfway houses.

BEARD, J. H., SCHMIDT, J. R., SMITH, M. M., and DINCIN, J., "Three Aspects of Psychiatric Rehabilitation at Fountain House." *Mental Hygiene,* 48(1):11-21, January, 1964.
Deals with purpose and function of New York's Fountain House; discusses the vocational rehabilitation program, the residential (apartment) program, and ways to reduce dropout rate.

BEARD, J. H., and GOLDMAN, E., "Major Problems of Halfway House Programs." *Rehabilitation Record,* 5(2):14-16, March-April, 1964.
Relates to the types of patients and services of most benefit in the halfway house.

BENNET, W. I., "Students, Patients Share Halfway House." *Rehabilitation Record,* 5(2):21-24, March-April, 1964.
A description of Wellmet, Inc., a halfway house in Cambridge, Massachusetts, written by a former "student-resident."

BLACK, B. J., "Psychiatric Rehabilitation in the Community," in L. Bellak, ed., *Handbook of Community Psychiatry and Community Mental Health* (New York, Grune & Stratton, 1964), pp. 248-264.
Covers the spectrum of hospital and community services and treatment modalities as well as the extent of psychiatric disability and patient motivation. Reports on ex-patients' clubs, day and night hospitals, halfway houses, foster care, and vocational rehabilitation. Details of Altro Health and Rehabilitation Services are given.

BOAG, T. J., "Psychiatric Hospital as Center of Hospital-Community Activities," in M. Greenblatt, D. J. Levinson, and G. L. Klerman, eds., *Mental Patients in Transition: Steps in Hospital-Community Rehabilitation* (Springfield, Illinois, Charles C. Thomas, 1961), pp. 59-71.
Describes the development of the Allan Memorial Institute of Psychiatry in Canada and its hospital-based and nonhospital-based aftercare facilities.

BROOKS, G. W., "Opening a Rehabilitation House," in M. Greenblatt and B. Simon, eds., *Rehabilitation of the Mentally Ill: Social and Economic*

Aspects. Publication No. 58, American Association for the Advancement of Science, Washington, D.C., 1959, pp. 127-139.

Discusses vocational rehabilitation program in Vermont, including the problems encountered in opening a rehabilitation house for chronic schizophrenic women.

CHITTICK, R. A., *et al., The Vermont Story: Rehabilitation of Chronic Schizophrenic Patients.* Burlington, Vermont, Queen City Printers, January, 1961.

The Vermont State Hospital rehabilitation program, including three halfway houses for ex-patients.

Community Care of the Mentally Ill: A Selected Annotated Bibliography. National Clearinghouse for Mental Health Information, U.S. Department of Health, Education, and Welfare, Public Health Service, Bethesda, Maryland, September, 1966.

DEAN, R. L., "The Mistakes That Make a Halfway House." *SK&F Psychiatric Reporter,* 14:9-10, May-June, 1964.

Describes the Eleanor B. Gutman Rehabilitation House in Portland, Oregon, which emphasizes occupational training and placement; and discusses the problems encountered during the development and the insights gained.

DONIGER, J., *Woodley House: Tenth Annual Report.* 1969.

History, operations, financial aspects, and goals of Woodley House, Washington, D.C.

DONIGER, J., ROTHWELL, N. D., and COHEN, R., "Case Study of a Halfway House." *Mental Hospitals,* 14(4): 191-199, April, 1963.

Description of Woodley House (Washington, D.C.), a psychiatric halfway house utilizing "a family-like setting."

ELDRED, D. M., "Problems of Opening a Rehabilitation House." *Mental Hospitals,* 8(5):20-21, September, 1957.

Reports on the beginning of the Vermont rehabilitation project.

ELDRED, D. M., BROOKS, G. W., DEANE, W. N., and TAYLOR, M. B., "The Rehabilitation of the Hospitalized Mentally Ill—The Vermont Story." *American Journal of Public Health,* 52(1):39-46, January, 1962.

Deals with the Vermont State Hospital rehabilitation project.

FISHER, S. H., *et al.,* "Rehabilitation of the Mental Hospital Patient: The Fountain House Programme." *International Journal of Social Psychiatry,* 4(4), Spring, 1960.

A description of Fountain House in New York, including its program of leasing apartments for members to live in.

GILL, W. S., "San Antonio's Halfway House." *Hospital and Community Psychiatry,* 18(9):43, September, 1967.

Describes halfway house sponsored by the Bexar County Association for Mental Health; origins, referrals, program, residents, and a follow-up study.

GOMNESS, C. D., "Supervision of Rutland Corner House: A Transitional Residence," in M. Greenblatt, D. J. Levinson, and G. L. Klerman, eds., *Mental Patients in Transition: Steps in Hospital-Community Rehabilitation* (Springfield, Illinois, Charles C. Thomas, 1961), pp. 83-88.
Description of Rutland Corner House, Brookline, Massachusetts, including rules, financial information, and criteria for admitting and discharging residents.

GREENBLATT, M., and SIMON, B., eds., *Rehabilitation of the Mentally Ill: Social and Economic Aspects.* Publication No. 58, American Association for the Advancement of Science, Washington, D.C., 1959.
Presents papers prepared for a conference on rehabilitation held in Indianapolis in December, 1957.

GUMRUKCU, P., and MIKELS, E., "Combating Post-Hospital Bends: Patterns of Success and Failure in a Psychiatric Halfway House." *Mental Hygiene,* 49(2):244-249, April, 1965.
Reports on the accommodative patterns toward self-sustaining employment of forty ex-mental patients who resided at Conard House in San Francisco. Compares Conard to other halfway houses, and describes the research methodology. A typology of success and failure is developed.

"A Halfway House with Family Feeling." *Mental Hospitals,* 12(12):22-23, December, 1961.
Concerns Rutland Corner House, Brookline, Massachusetts.

HUSETH, B., "Halfway Houses, A New Rehabilitation Measure." *Mental Hospitals,* 9(8):5-6, 8-9, October, 1958.
Explains the halfway house mechanism—planning, financing, location, selection of residents, criteria for discharge, staffing, and hospital relations.

HUSETH, B., "What Is a Halfway House? Functions and Types." *Mental Hygiene,* 45(1):116-121, January, 1961.
Gives definitions, structure, and functions of the halfway house in the United States and England.

HUSETH, B., "England's Halfway Houses." *Mental Hospitals,* 13(8):422-424, August, 1962.
Discusses various types of halfway houses for patients with different anticipated goals and the problems involved in setting up a halfway house.

JANSEN, E., "The Role of the Halfway House in Community Mental Health Programs in the United Kingdom and America." *American Journal of Psychiatry,* 126(10):1498-1504, April, 1970.
Discusses various approaches to halfway house operations, including the emergence of a philosophy arising from an experimental project in England and the subsequent establishment of a halfway house organization. Reviews problems and government attitudes toward halfway

houses in the U.K. and U.S. and makes suggestions for initiating a halfway house program.

KANTOR, D., and GREENBLATT, M., "Wellmet: Halfway to Community Rehabilitation." *Mental Hospitals,* 13(3):146-152, March, 1962.
Gives an account of Wellmet, Inc., Cambridge, Massachusetts, a halfway house for chronic mental patients, run by students. Two case histories are included.

KEMPTON, M., "Halfway House." *The New Republic,* 148(12):8-10, March 23, 1963.
Describes the Brooklyn (New York) Pre-Release Guidance Center, a halfway house for offenders.

LANDY, D., "Exploration in Residential After-Care of Psychiatric Patients: A Men's Halfway House." *The International Journal of Social Psychiatry,* 6(1&2):132-149, Summer, 1960.
Describes and analyzes an experiment by a hospital in transitional residential aftercare of the discharged male psychiatric patients. The method and scope of the experiment are explained, as are the history, finances, selection process, and expectations of the halfway house. Several case histories are given.

LANDY, D., "Rutland Corner House: Case Study of a Halfway House." *The Journal of Social Issues,* 16(2):27-32, April, 1960.
Includes the history, organization, residents, supervision, and preliminary evaluation of Rutland Corner House in Brookline, Mass.

LANDY, D., and GREENBLATT, M., *Halfway House: A Sociocultural and Clinical Study of Rutland Corner House, A Transitional After-Care Residence for Female Psychiatric Patients.* U.S. Department of Health, Education, and Welfare, Washington, D.C., 1965.
A detailed discussion of Rutland Corner House (Brookline, Massachusetts) including a history of the house, the purpose of this study, and the residents.

LANDY, D., and WECHSLER, H., "Common Assumptions, Dimensions, and Problems of Pathway Organizations." *The Journal of Social Issues,* 16(2):70-78, April, 1960.
Explores transitional agencies, including the problems they face.

LANDY, D., "A Halfway House for Women: Preliminary Report of a Study," in M. Greenblatt, D. J. Levinson, and G. L. Klerman, eds., *Mental Patients in Transition: Steps in Hospital-Community Rehabilitation* (Springfield, Illinois, Charles C. Thomas, 1961), pp. 94-103.
A preliminary report of some results of a study conducted over a two-year period of the structure and function of Rutland Corner House (Brookline, Massachusetts), including: *a*) a follow-up study of former residents; *b*) a study of the house; *c*) a history of the development of the house.

LEWIS, F., and KRAFT, A., "Wellmet: Halfway to Community Rehabilitation." *Mental Hospitals,* 14(3):146-152, March, 1963.
A description of Wellmet, a halfway house in Cambridge, Massachusetts.

LOETHER, H. J., *A Social Psychological Study of Role Shifts and Outcomes of Halfway House Residents.* California State College, Dominguez Hills, California. (Mimeograph, undated.)
Tells how the halfway house should help the former patient shift from the sick role to a well role. Includes results of a study from 1964-1966.

LYMAN, S., "History and Organization of the Rutland Corner (Halfway) House," in M. Greenblatt, D. J. Levinson, G. L. Klerman, eds., *Mental Patients in Transition: Steps in Hospital-Community Rehabilitation* (Springfield, Illinois, Charles C. Thomas, 1961), pp. 77-82.
Brief history of Rutland Corner House, Brookline, Massachusetts.

MAEDA, E. M., and ROTHWELL, N. D., *Discussion, Listing, and Bibliography of Psychiatric Halfway Houses in the United States.* Psychiatric Studies and Projects No. 9, Mental Hospital Service of the American Psychiatric Association, Washington, D.C., September, 1963.

METCALF, G. W., "Woodley House—A Pioneering Mental Health Project." *Medical Annals of the District of Columbia,* March, 1962.
Description of Woodley House, Washington, D.C.

MIKELS, E., and GUMRUKCU, P., "A Therapeutic Halfway Hostel." *Mental Hospitals,* 14(4):219, April, 1963.
Describes Conard House, San Francisco, the residents, staff, social atmosphere, and a study of thirty residents.

MUTH, L. T., *After-Care Services in the United States: A Progress Report of State Hospital Programs.* Veterans Administration Hospital, Huntington, West Virginia, October 1, 1960 (Mimeograph).
Gives responses of seventy hospitals in forty states to a questionnaire regarding progress in aftercare since 1957. Names and details are given for each of the participating hospitals.

OGILBY, A. P., "Interviews with Two Former Residents of Rutland Corner House," in M. Greenblatt, D. J. Levinson, and G. L. Klerman, eds., *Mental Patients in Transition: Steps in Hospital-Community Rehabilitation* (Springfield, Illinois, Charles C. Thomas, 1961), pp. 89-93.
Case histories of, and discussions with, two former residents of Rutland Corner House, Brookline, Massachusetts.

OLTMAN, J. E., and FRIEDMAN, S., "Results at a 'Halfway House.'" *Diseases of the Nervous System,* 25(5):317-318, May, 1964.
A résumé of what has happened to 189 patients transferred from a state hospital to a halfway house (unidentified), between 1956 and 1961.

PATTERSON, C. H., "A Suggested Blueprint for Psychiatric Rehabilitation." *Community Mental Health Journal,* 1(1):61-68, Spring, 1965.
Expresses some developments in the area of rehabilitation and offers a

plan for organization of services in a community-based social psychiatric rehabilitation center.

RAUSH, H. L., and RAUSH, C., *The Halfway House Movement: A Search for Sanity*. New York, Appleton-Century-Crofts, 1968.
Defines the halfway house and looks at its development, function, structure, operation, and future. Forty halfway houses are included in this study carried out in 1963.

RICHMOND, C., "Halfway House and Day Hospital Complement Each Other." *Hospital and Community Psychiatry,* 19(3):78-79, March, 1968.
Describes Miramonte Mental Health Services in Palo Alto, California; the day hospital, the halfway house (Harvey House), the patients, and the program.

ROSS, F., *Conard House: A Psychiatric Halfway House.* (Mimeograph, undated.)
Complete story of Conard House, San Francisco.

ROTHWELL, N. D., and DONIGER, J. M., "The Halfway House," in J. H. Masserman, ed., *Current Psychiatric Therapies,* Vol. 5 (New York, Grune & Stratton, Inc., 1965), pp. 240-246.
A general survey of psychiatric halfway houses with a detailed description of Woodley House, Washington, D.C.

ROTHWELL, N. D., and DONIGER, J. M., *The Psychiatric Halfway House: A Case Study.* Springfield, Illinois, Charles C. Thomas, 1966.
The story of Woodley House, Washington, D.C.—how it began, its organization, operation, staffing, and residents.

RUTMAN, I. D., "Ex-Mental Patients in Halfway Houses: Origin and Present Status." *Rehabilitation Record,* 5(2):10-13, March-April, 1964.
Origins, development, and present facilities for aftercare are discussed along with finances, characteristics, and psychiatry's role.

Selected Bibliography on Halfway Houses. National Clearinghouse for Mental Health Information, U.S. Department of Health, Education, and Welfare, Public Health Service, Bethesda, Maryland, September, 1963.

SHARP, G., "A Perspective on the Function of the Psychiatric Halfway House." *Mental Hygiene,* 48(4):552-557, October, 1964.
Discusses the function of the halfway house as an aid in the adjustment from hospital to community.

SHUBIN, S., "New Horizons at Horizon House." *SK&F Psychiatric Reporter,* 18:19-21, January-February, 1965.
Describes the rehabilitation facilities at Horizon House in Philadelphia, including a residence for 22 men.

TUNAKAN, B., and SCHAFER, I. J., "The Community Boarding House as a Transitional Residence During Aftercare," in J. H. Masserman, ed., *Current Psychiatric Therapies,* Vol. 5 (New York, Grune & Stratton, Inc., 1965), pp. 235-239.

Describes the use of two boardinghouses (in association with the Nebraska Psychiatric Institute) which place psychiatric patients amid normal tenants. Gives history, operation, eligibility criteria, financial arrangements, and experience to date.

WAYNE, G. J., "An Evaluation of New Trends in Psychiatric Hospitals." *Mental Hospitals,* 13(1):10-15, January, 1962.
Discusses the need for such transitional care services as foster care homes, day and night hospitals, halfway houses, sheltered workshops, and ex-patients' clubs. The functions and relationships to the hospital of these services are listed. Edgemont House in Los Angeles is described.

WAYNE, G. J., and RICHARDSON, I. K., "The Halfway House: How It Serves as a Pathway Agency for the Psychiatric Patient." *Psychiatric Quarterly,* 37(1):67-96, January, 1963.
Reports on the first twenty months at Edgemont House (Los Angeles), including twenty individual case histories and evaluative comments.

WAYNE, G. J., "The Special Contributions of a Hospital Halfway House." *Mental Hospitals,* 14(8):440-442, August, 1963.
Edgemont Hospital, Los Angeles, California.

WAYNE, G. J., "The Hospital-Affiliated Halfway House," in J. H. Masserman, ed., *Current Psychiatric Therapies,* Vol. 4 (New York, Grune & Stratton, Inc., 1964), pp. 213-217.
Reports on Edgemont House (affiliated with Edgemont Hospital, Los Angeles), and lists the advantages of such an affiliation. Deals with activities, goals, staffing, selection of patients, and criteria for success and failure.

WECHSLER, H., "Halfway Houses for Former Mental Patients: A Survey." *The Journal of Social Issues,* 16(2):20-26, April, 1960.
General discussion of halfway houses detailing function, residents, staffing, types of houses, and evaluational problems.

WECHSLER, H., "Transitional Residence for Former Mental Patients: A Survey of Halfway Houses and Related Rehabilitation Facilities." *Mental Hygiene,* 45(1):65-76, January, 1961.
Depicts use of transitional residence in aftercare. Contains the information mentioned in the above description.

WILDER, J. F., KESSEL, M., and CAULFIELD, S. C., "Follow-Up of a 'High Expectations' Halfway House." *American Journal of Psychiatry,* 124(8):1085-1091, February, 1968.
Describes the first year at Overing Apartments, Bronx, New York, a halfway house. Outcomes of 42 tenants are evaluated.

WOLKON, G. H., and TANAKA, H. T., "Professionals' Views on the Need for Psychiatric Aftercare Services." *Community Mental Health Journal,* 1(3):262-270, Fall, 1965.

The need for aftercare services for recently released patients is discussed in interviews with psychiatrists and social workers at four state hospitals. Suggestions discussed for new and existing aftercare facilities include strengthening of referral procedures and a more efficient organization.

WRIGHT, F. H., BROWN, H. E., MACDANIEL, J. R., and ENGSTROM, F. H., "A Descriptive Report on 65 Halfway House Patients Over a Two-and-One-Half-Year Period." *International Journal of Social Psychiatry,* 12(4):289-292, Autumn, 1966.

Deals with 65 patients from a Veterans Administration hospital assigned to three halfway houses in Gulfport from January 1961 to July 1963, in an attempt to determine various criteria of success.